F.W. Webb

In the right place at the right time

by
John Chacksfield
FRAeS, FBIS, AFAIAA, C.Eng

THE OAKWOOD PRESS

© Oakwood Press & John Chacksfield 2007

British Library Cataloguing in Publication Data
A Record for this book is available from the British Library
ISBN 978 0 85361 657 3

Typeset by Oakwood Graphics.
Repro by Ford Graphics, Ringwood, Hants.
Printed by Cambrian Printers, Aberystwyth, Ceredigion.

'Precedent' class 2-4-0 No. 890 *Sir Hardman Earle.*   *John Alsop Collection*

Title page: 'Precursor' class 2-4-0 No. 1152 *Arab.*   *John Alsop Collection*

Front cover: Webb 'Dreadnought' class locomotive speeds over Bushey troughs as it heads the 'Wild Irishman' express.   *John Alsop Collection*
Rear cover, top: Webb 0-4-0ST at Dhu Stone Works, Clee Hill.   *John Alsop Collection*
Rear cover, bottom: Webb 'Alfred the Great' class 4-cylinder compound 4-4-0 No. 1955 *Hannibal.*   *John Alsop Collection*

Published by The Oakwood Press (Usk), P.O. Box 13, Usk, Mon., NP15 1YS.
E-mail: sales@oakwoodpress.co.uk
Website: www.oakwoodpress.co.uk

Contents

Frank Webb. A signed photograph taken about 1885.   *Author's Collection*

Foreword

F.W. Webb was one of the great railway engineers of the 19th century. When still in his early thirties, he was appointed head of the locomotive department of the London & North Western Railway (LNWR) and retained the position until he retired over 30 years later. It was a time of great expansion, innovation and technical progress on the railways in general, and he ensured that the LNWR led the way, especially in any matters where he saw there were advantages to be gained. He was a pioneer in the use of steel, for instance, designed new machine tools and improved production processes, and was a prolific inventor, with numerous patents to his credit. He was responsible for Crewe works, with all its functions, products and ramifications, of which locomotive design and maintenance were only a part. Under his leadership the works was expanded to the level at which the *Railway Magazine* described it as the 'most famous works in the world'. F.W. Webb's contribution was immense and not for nothing was he known as the 'King of Crewe'.

Inevitably in such an important position held for such a long period of time, errors of judgement were occasionally made. More accurately, decisions were made with the best of intentions, which were seen later to have been errors (hindsight is a wonderful thing), and some have led to controversy on which views are still expressed today. An example of the latter particularly is the use of compounding, but another, which makes the point more clearly, is the reluctance to adopt the automatic vacuum brake, which came about simply because of the wish to avoid the extra expense it entailed. Webb has been described as 'penny-pinching', and Moon, his Chairman, as a 'skinflint'. But it is easy nowadays, when vast sums of money are squandered on 'private' companies to maintain the myth that railways are operating 'commercially' for the benefit of 'customers', to forget that in the 19th century proper capitalist principles applied. Strict control of costs was essential, especially in a large organization such as the LNWR, if income were to exceed expenditure by the margin necessary to run the company properly, pay dividends to the shareholders and raise more capital when required. It is an indication of Moon's success, aided by Webb's management of his department, that the LNWR came to be known in the city of London as the 'Premier Line'. In other words, its shares could be relied upon more than those of any other railway company to pay their dividends. If Moon and Webb had failed in this respect, critics would have had much better reasons for their adverse criticism.

In view of Webb's importance, it is surprising that no biography has ever been published. Much has been written about him both in his lifetime and since. Numerous articles appeared in the technical journals and enthusiast publications of the day, and he was frequently mentioned in the local newspapers at Crewe, for example, while even more has perhaps been published about him since in enthusiast publications and indeed is still being written about him. In addition, a vast amount of information resides in archive sources, especially in the National Archives at Kew and the National Railway Museum at York, but in several others also. Several researchers have explored aspects which interest them but unfortunately have shied away from any attempt to cover the whole subject and even to write up the results of their work. Quite possibly, it is simply the huge quantity of material available that has deterred potential biographers.

Now at last, and with great good fortune, John Chacksfield, an experienced biographer of railway engineers, has been undaunted by the task and has tackled it with energy and enthusiasm. At the outset, he resolved to take an impartial stance on controversial matters and to form judgements based only on the balance of evidence. He has produced a thoroughly readable account which will become essential reading for anyone interested in the railway history of the 19th century, as well as containing much of interest to LNWR specialists also. It is to be hoped that others will now be encouraged into print with the results of their biographical researches. But John Chacksfield has led the way, for which we must all be grateful. Congratulations to him!

Edward Talbot
Gnosall,
Stafford

Preamble

Francis William Webb was much maligned at the end of his career and after his death, a feature which has persisted for nearly a century. It is high time this factor was investigated to correct any wrong created by such adverse criticism. This was one of the drivers behind my decision to write this biography, another being that no attempt has been made to fill the gap in railway history left by the lack of such a book about the life and times of a very eminent engineer. One wonders how the adverse criticism affected the lack of a suitable treatise on the life of a clearly competent and highly regarded engineer who held down one of the key jobs, that of Locomotive Superintendent, and latterly Chief Mechanical Engineer, on the London & North Western Railway for over 30 years. However, once research had commenced, some fragments of previously unpublished data relevant to Webb's background began to surface, which put a different slant on matters associated with his career. The more I dug into this limited information, the more I was certain that Webb has been depicted incorrectly as a mentally unstable character towards the end of his career. Medical science has advanced considerably since those days and we can put more correct diagnoses on symptoms previously given wrong labels. Stubbornness and mental instability do not always go hand in hand, the former is allied to a belief in one's reasoning, the latter is too random sensibly to have reason as a root cause. Yet earlier authorities have seen fit to equate the two in their analysis of certain happenings towards the end of an eminent career. I hope that my interpretations will put right a great wrong at last. The man deserves it.

Introduction and Acknowledgements

Much has been written about Francis William Webb, giant of Crewe, and his locomotives, and too much in a derogatory sense. Surprisingly, no-one has attempted to set down the story of his life in a biographical context. It has always been his engineering exploits that have commanded attention and, as a result, the background of his personal life faded due to excessive analysis of his few lesser creations. This latter at the expense of his undoubtedly competent dealing with the design and production requirements of the London & North Western Railway's locomotive stock for over 30 years.

To be selected as one of Webb's pupils provided an opportunity to be advised by one of the great Victorian engineers. Wise advice it was, and many eminent railway engineers were to benefit from their association with him. Likewise, a premium apprenticeship at Crewe also brought the association with Webb to the lasting benefit of those who listened to and followed the precepts of a truly sound engineering perception. The legacy of Crewe ideals and methods was thereby spread to many of the other railways throughout Britain, Ireland and a large number of other countries of the world by such people as Aspinall, Ivatt, Gresley, Hughes and Hoy, amongst others, by these associations. I have taken the liberty to add an Appendix to detail the eventual positions of eminence reached by those and other persons.

A feature of Webb's advancement to high office was the fact that he benefited from unscheduled happenings, hence the sub-title to this biography of 'In the right place at the right time'. Undoubtedly his childhood upbringing in the confines of a country vicarage, surrounded by a close-knit family, helped him formulate a tidy mind which clearly influenced his in-built skills as an organizer and administrator. One Victorian attribute associated with 'sons of the Church' was the certain knowledge of 'a gentlemanly upbringing', for the LNWR Board still held this as a basic requirement for any high LNWR officer. 'First a gentleman, secondly an LNWR man' as the Chairman from 1861, (Sir) Richard Moon, was known to have specified.

In terms of his locomotive designs, Webb was responsible for the construction of some 3,482 locomotives, new and rebuilt, of which 494 were of compounds. His simple expansion designs, although mentioned as being small in size, according to earlier contemporary reports, were in fact no smaller than equivalent designs on the other railways. However, they were robust and reliable and helped the LNWR to achieve a good operating economy enabling the railway to finance the expansion of Crewe works to a level appropriate to the productive demands required. Indeed, for all his career, the LNWR enjoyed a reputation for punctuality, and when any railway gets that as an example of its efficiency, the slightest delay to a popular train tends to get blown out of all proportion. So much criticism has been levelled at the compound locomotive side of things that the competence of the simple designs has been allowed to fade into the background. It was the sheer capacity of these locomotives to be driven hard and achieve punctuality that provided Webb with one aspect of the catalyst to experiment with, and introduce, the compound designs. Also, with his outstanding expertise in the works area, the means of production were always at a suitable level to satisfy all demands made upon them.

Webb never married, and so lacked the influence of a family around him, but several other eminent engineers adopted a similar way of life. Their work was their family and, in some cases, this made them somewhat rough in their dealings with the more personal matters of their subordinates. However, Frank Webb was by no means ungenerous, sharing not only his knowledge with others, but, upon his death, his considerable wealth was apportioned between his relations, personal friends and the many institutions and societies he was associated with, both locally and nationally, with a very substantial residue to set up an orphanage. There was also a reported background of hereditary illness which was thought to have had some influence on his bachelor status, such was the Victorian attitude towards the possibility of inherited problems. However, this seems doubtful on two counts, firstly he was not a confirmed bachelor, women did enter his life as we shall see and, secondly, as research by a retired GP has produced no proof of any such problems in the family. Unfortunately, those who were aware of this rumour all too quickly allied their analysis of Webb's final days in office to it as a root cause, in the form of a mental condition, of his retirement. However, this latter feature appears a most unlikely cause, as we shall see. Other facts concerning Webb's forebears seem to point to another feature likely to have affected the interpretation of his life in some way.

All in all, a career and life well worth writing about, to bring together some of the most important phases of the development of the LNWR in the latter half of the 19th century, as the railways in Britain rose to their zenith.

I would like to acknowledge my debt of gratitude to those who have assisted in my task of collecting the information needed to produce this biography. The LNWR Society lunch at Crewe introduced me to many interested parties who have perused my draft text and made useful suggestions and corrections. In that context, I would single out Roger Bell, Peter Davis and Ted Talbot in particular. Ted Talbot also provided the excellent foreword. The illustrations come from a wide range of sources. Many historical pictures were provided by John Alsop, Ted Talbot, others came from Jim Jarvis and, of course, the LNWR Society collection.

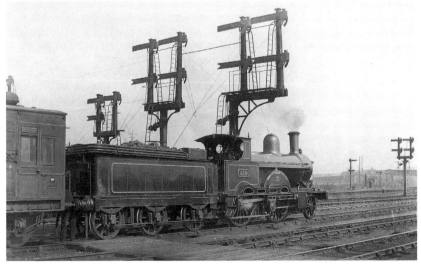

'Experiment' class compound No. 519 *Shooting Star* is seemingly deserted by its crew, Chester, 1901.   *R.S. Carpenter Collection*

Chapter One

The Beginnings

The village of Tixall, some four miles east of Stafford, sits in the Trent Valley not far from the parallel paths of the Trent-Mersey Canal and the River Trent. It still is a smallish village, and has a small, but well kept parish church, dedicated to St John the Baptist. Our story begins around this church, for it was here that the Revd William Webb assumed the living in 1831. He was to remain Rector for over 50 years and raise his family, of four boys and one girl, in the Rectory, before they embarked on their individual lives.

This particular branch of the Webb family has a long history of association with the town of Stafford and the story starts with one Henry Webb, who was born at Harlaston, near Tamworth, in 1748. Henry's family were, it appears, quite high up the social scale so it was not surprising that in 1777 he was to become a partner in the bank at Stafford founded by John Stevenson some 40 years previously. In 1791, as affairs in France began to affect British society, with rioting taking place in Birmingham, he became acquainted with Elizabeth Heath and, within a few months, their association blossomed into a deep mutual affection such that they began a 32 year life together. She was some 22 years his junior.

Over the following 17 years Elizabeth bore Henry 10 children, six girls and four boys, all of whom were baptised with Henry listed as father in the relevant documentation. Henry's choice of lifestyle (he and Elizabeth appeared never to have married) had no effect on his business life and he was to remain a partner in the bank until retiring in 1826, to continue living at Forebridge Hall, the home he had occupied for many years. He also had been appointed a high sheriff in Staffordshire in 1810.

Elizabeth died in 1823 and Henry, after just a few months, then married Rachel, the widow of Thomas Garrett of Basingstoke. She had been the matron of a Lunatic Asylum. The strange thing is, when Henry himself passed on in 1831, he was buried alongside Elizabeth, Rachel being buried elsewhere when she herself died. This example of relationships of about 200 years ago, by modern standards, is nothing out of the ordinary, save the number of offspring produced. It was not reported by the limited media of the day and probably could be swept under the carpet quite easily.

To return to the 10 children, the one of interest is William, the youngest son, born in 1806. Following his education at Brewood School, he entered Trinity College, Cambridge where he obtained a BA in 1828. In those days this degree was adequate to allow further study for him to be ordained into the Church of England as Deacon in 1829 and Priest in 1830. He then obtained the post of Curate in the parish of Armitage, near Lichfield for one year. In 1831 he was inducted into the Parish of Tixall. The Rectory and its associated living was in the patronage of Earl Talbot and clearly this was quite a lucrative placing, despite the fact that the population of the village in that year was a mere 176 souls.

The Church of St John the Baptist, Tixall.   *Author*

Tixall Rectory as it is today. The home where Frank Webb was born and brought up.
                                                                 Author's Collection

The newly installed Revd Webb wasted no time in providing himself with a wife. His brother George had, in 1828, married Lucy Georgiana Morgan from Lichfield, whose younger sister, Maria, William had begun to court. She and the Reverend were married in early 1832 and settled into the Rectory at Tixall. There were to be five children, Mary Elizabeth (1832), Arthur Henry (1834), Francis William (1836), Walter George (1838) and William James (1844). Once the family had been created the Revd Webb turned to a very important matter requiring his undivided attention, the rebuilding of his church. This major feat was accomplished in 1849, by which time the population of Tixall had increased to 200. Thus the Revd Webb had contributed some 25 per cent of this population growth, if one includes the import of his wife to the parish!

The child of note for our story is the second son, Francis William, born at Tixall Rectory on 21st May, 1836. He was to display a decided bent towards an engineering career from an early age, a fact which was noted by his father. One significant event which led his father to recognise this was the episode of the pony cart. At the age of 11, young Francis, from a few pieces of timber lying around and a couple of old wheels from a disused cart, built a pony cart which, 'When that was completed there was great joy in the village of Tixall, and the cart was exhibited on the village green, much to the admiration of the inhabitants'. Here we find the first thread of evidence of his pride in exhibiting his creations, a trait which never left him. He also got himself involved in the rebuilding of his father's church by persuading the masons to let him try his hand at their work: 'In fact, several parts of the Church were finished by him, and some figures sculpted entirely by himself'. For notable events in the year of his birth the one which stands out, in Britain, was the appearance in print of Charles Dickens' classic *Pickwick Papers*.

The Webb family. Standing are, *from left to right*, Frank and William. In front, Mary, Walter, Revd Webb, Arthur and Mrs Webb.   *Author's Collection*

As with all the other children, Francis was educated at home by his father. This education clearly was very thorough, for both Arthur and William went to Trinity College, Cambridge and became clergymen, and Walter became an Army officer rising to the rank of Colonel. In those days, it was not uncommon for the Clergy to undertake their own families' education at home. Francis, or Frank as he was known by close friends and the family, clearly was taught the basics by his father in a very competent way, for it enabled him to be granted a premium apprenticeship under Francis Trevithick, the then Locomotive Superintendent at the Crewe works of the LNWR, commencing on 11th August, 1851. The Reverend Webb must have been rather delighted in the varying choice of careers of his sons.

However, there had been one significant development taking place locally during Frank's childhood, which probably influenced his choice of the above career, and this was the construction of the Trent Valley Railway which was soon merged into the London & Birmingham Railway, Grand Junction Railway (GJR) and Manchester & Birmingham Railway empire. This amalgamation lived only briefly before the foundation of the LNWR in 1846. He would have spent much time watching the engineering tasks nearby as the railways established their hold on the provision of transport throughout the country. So many small boys have been motivated to consider railway engineering as a career from the examples presented to them by the sight of huge earthworks and hundreds of navvies shaping the countryside for railway tracks. The once tranquil countryside was then disturbed by the stirring sound of steam locomotives as they passed, seemingly intent on speeding their loads and passengers to their destinations.

Frank was to remain close to his family, particularly the elder of his three brothers, Arthur, who for many years, was to be a Canon based at St Paul's, Crewe, and conveniently to hand to be a key player in the episode surrounding Frank's enforced retirement in 1903.

Frank's new mentor, from whom he was to gather much useful information to further his career, Francis Trevithick, was the son of Richard Trevithick who has been called the father of the steam locomotive, in the form of the 1804 Pen-y-Daren locomotive. This historic locomotive had hauled 10 tons of iron and 70 men some nine miles along a plateway running between Pen-y-Daren Ironworks and Abercynon to win a 500 guineas wager for the Pen-y-Daren ironmaster from another local ironmaster, although whether this wager was ever paid has never been substantiated.

Francis Trevithick had been appointed the first Locomotive Superintendent at Crewe. Now, the early days of the LNWR were such that there were three production centres, at Crewe, Manchester and Wolverton, each with their own works and superintendent. This was hardly a recipe for economy, particularly as the costs involved in building up a major railway system required careful management. Initially, Frank took lodgings with a barber, Richard Shermen, whose premises and home were at the corner of Mill Street, and were very convenient for access to the works.

One of Frank's first recorded efforts at Crewe was nothing to do with his ultimate aim of being involved in the design and production of locomotives.

Shortly after arriving to commence his time, he had noticed that a fledgling cricket club had been set up in Crewe, and like most external organizations would be much used by the workforce. Cricket was one ball game which he enjoyed and very soon he had joined this club. Frank realised that a roller would be a useful tool for preparing pitches. He accordingly approached Trevithick about the possibility of making a roller in the works. Trevithick acquiesced, laying down just two provisos, these being that Webb did the job himself and that it did not take any of the workers off their normal jobs. He set to with a purpose and, in due course, Crewe Cricket Club became the proud possessor of Webb's first production exercise - a brand new roller. Trevithick also permitted the stumps and bails to be turned in the works.

The time in the works was a happy one for Frank, as he gathered his skills on the shop floor. Not afraid of making representation to the highest level, his apprenticeship under Trevithick was clearly of great benefit for the future. So far as technical education went, he attended evening classes provided at the nearby Mechanics Institute. This had grown from the early beginnings as a library and news-room for Grand Junction Railway employees to a purpose-built centre specifically provided 'to supply the working classes of Crewe the means of instruction in Science, Literature and the Arts'. The LNWR covered the running costs of this establishment. Much of the technical instruction was given by key people from Crewe works. In 1852, the then chief draughtsman, Wayte, took the class on mechanical drawing. Frank is thought to have been an attendee at this class, but unfortunately no records remain to confirm this. However, it is on record in the Chaloner book *The Social and Economic Development of Crewe* that Frank, from a very early time of his apprenticeship, was teaching at the Institute himself, and continued to do so until 1866. He was to remain an enthusiastic supporter of Technical education all his life. By the time his final year was under way he had been placed in the drawing office, Trevithick having decided that his maximum benefit to the LNWR would be on that side of affairs. The chief draughtsman was then a William Williams, who was reputed to be the Williams who had schemed the original Stephenson link motion when employed at the Stephenson works in Newcastle in around 1841.

The apprenticeship ended in 1856 and Trevithick wrote a telling note to the works sub-committee: 'Frank Webb, draughtsman in my office, is out of his apprenticeship, and that he is an exceedingly respectable young man and his services are very valuable...' He then recommended a permanent position for Webb in the drawing office at £2 per week.

Webb's first significant tasks as a fully-fledged member of the design team came under Ramsbottom, who had succeeded Trevithick in 1857. This succession was tinged with some rather awkward treatment of the then two Northern Locomotive Superintendents on the LNWR, for the Northern (Crewe) Division and the North Eastern (Manchester) Division, Trevithick and Ramsbottom respectively. The Board of the LNWR wished to bring together these two works under one management in order to trim costs. One head had to roll, and it was Trevithick who lost out, being given a 'golden handshake' of £3,000. This gift was in view of his long service, honourable character and the good opinion of his achievements held by two or three Directors. Clearly, there

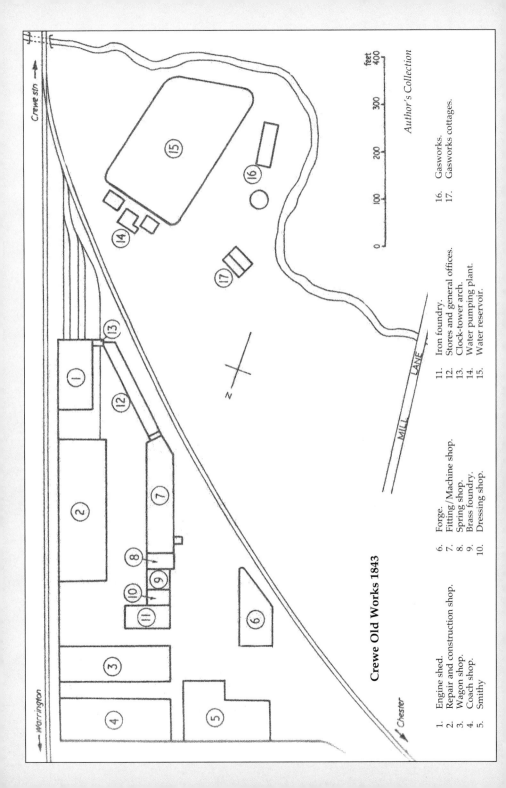

Crewe Old Works 1843

1. Engine shed.
2. Repair and construction shop.
3. Wagon shop.
4. Coach shop.
5. Smithy
6. Forge.
7. Fitting/Machine shop.
8. Spring shop.
9. Brass foundry.
10. Dressing shop.
11. Iron foundry.
12. Stores and general offices.
13. Clock-tower arch.
14. Water pumping plant.
15. Water reservoir.
16. Gasworks.
17. Gasworks cottages.

Author's Collection

feet
0   100   200   300   400

← Warrington

Crewe sth →

Chester →

MILL LANE

N

were those on the Board who were convinced that his handling of matters at Crewe fell short of their own desires. He had been a popular Superintendent in the works, but had neglected to organize matters such that locomotive and stores accounting procedures could give a clear picture as to the true situation. However, his popularity within the works and Crewe itself was qualified by the presentation of £500 worth of plate at a special dinner arranged to bid him farewell.

Ramsbottom, born in 1814, was the son of a cotton spinner whose mill was fitted with one of the first steam engine units for the task of providing power. He started his engineering career by being trained by his father in the intricacies of power loom servicing and construction. This enabled him eventually to get a position as a journeyman on textile machinery produced by the Manchester works of Sharp, Roberts. At these works he met two early engineering pioneers, Richard Roberts and Charles Beyer. Sharp, Roberts had their locomotive side under the command of Beyer, who quickly saw to it that Ramsbottom was transferred to that field. Three years under Beyer plus a glowing recommendation gave him a position of locomotive running foreman on the Manchester & Birmingham Railway and so on to the Locomotive Superintendency of the North Eastern Division of the LNWR. Ramsbottom, out of his many inventions for improving the steam locomotive, is, perhaps, best remembered for his design of safety valve which was adopted by many of the major railways. It became virtually a standard component until largely superseded by the Ross Pop safety valve in the early years of the 20th century.

Alongside all this was ranged the Southern Division at Wolverton, with McConnell as Locomotive Superintendent there. This latter works was, eventually, to be absorbed into Crewe, so far as locomotive matters were concerned. This had been agreed in principle by the Board as far back as 1855 and remained tabled for future implementation.

Three Locomotive Superintendents. Seated in the centre are Webb (in hat), Trevithick and Ramsbottom.   *E. Talbot Collection*

An early example of the 'DX' class 0-6-0, No. 49. *LNWR Society Collection*

'DX' 0-6-0 No. 3312 in largely unrebuilt state, apart from addition of cab *c.*1885.

R.S. Carpenter Collection

The revised Northern Division and relatively unaffected Southern Division thus prepared to do battle for the ultimate choice of the single works covering the whole railway. Ramsbottom and McConnell prepared individual reports on their Divisions suggesting how matters between them could be arranged to make best use of locomotives and crews. However, in the background there appeared a man who was to have a great say in such policy matters in the future. This was Richard Moon, the future Chairman of the Board.

Moon had, up to 1858, been Chairman of the Stores Committee, which body was merged with the Locomotive Committee in that year, thus giving him a large say in locomotive affairs. He was very keen on cost savings wherever possible and the idea of having two Locomotive Superintendents was not only expensive, but, with two differing personalities, a recipe for conflict which he felt could affect the railway's costs. He had ultimate confidence in the organizational skills and strict discipline of Ramsbottom, but little time for McConnell. The latter's estimates of costs involved some considerable disagreements with Moon, who by 1861 was Chairman of the Board and engineered the resignation of the Southern Division Superintendent in February 1862. The door was now open for a complete reorganization of all locomotive affairs at Crewe.

Whilst all this was taking place, Ramsbottom was beginning his reorganization at Crewe of the discipline and manufacturing standards. Frank Webb was still in the drawing office and the early major tasks to come his way were, firstly, the design work on a standard 0-6-0 goods locomotive, to become the famous 'DX' class, and secondly to design the rebuild of the unusual 2-2-2 *Cornwall* which had lain largely unused since appearing in the Great Exhibition of 1851. A most unusual design, the original locomotive had the boiler mounted below the driving wheel axle, the underlying reason being to obtain as low a centre of gravity as possible. But this layout presented many problems, particularly in the provision of an adequate ash-pan under the firebox. This exercise to rebuild the experimental locomotive had an ulterior motive, in that it paved the way for a future development of Ramsbottom, that of a new express 2-2-2. It was, apart from the 8 ft 6 in. driving wheels and sundry details, a prototype for that project.

In September 1858 the first two 'DXs' appeared and immediately proved their worth, being joined by three others before the year's end. The rebuilt *Cornwall* also appeared at the end of that year, having now acquired a 'DX' boiler and conventional layout. Then something happened to cause a change in the drawing office, Williams died suddenly. A new chief draughtsman was urgently needed. Due to his heavy involvement on the successful 'DX' design and *Cornwall* rebuild, coupled with his promotion to leading draughtsman on the new express 2-2-2, which became known as the 'Problem' class, the position was given to Frank. He commenced his new responsibilities on 1st March, 1859, the salary being £140 per year. He was only 22, but clearly showing considerable promise on design matters.

In his new position Frank came into frequent contact with Ramsbottom and, clearly, the two got on well, with the latter making a mental note to encourage the former whenever the situation presented itself. Ramsbottom was one of those exceptional engineers who recognised ability when he saw it and was not afraid of encouraging it. The Crewe works were soon to become the premier production site for LNWR locomotives and there was much to be done in expansion and reorganization over the next few years. Ramsbottom felt that a person with Frank's ability would be of great use in helping organize what he had planned for the works scene.

John Ramsbottom, Locomotive Superintendent from 1857-71.   *Author's Collection*

Chapter Two

From Design to Production and the Bolton Move

After a mere two years as chief draughtsman, Webb received a further promotion, on 1st September, 1861, to the position of Chief Indoor Assistant, or Works Manager, as it was to become known, the salary being £180 per year which by November of that year had risen to £220. His organizational skills needed tapping and Ramsbottom, having found a suitable replacement chief draughtsman in 25-year-old Thomas Stubbs, recommended this change to the Works Committee to be effective from September 1861. Stubbs was another high-flyer of considerable skill who had started under Ramsbottom at the North Eastern Division's works at Longsight and had been brought with him to Crewe in 1857 and placed in the drawing office. These promotions were occasioned by the sudden resignation of the previous Works Manager, one Thomas Hunt, who left the country to take up the position of Locomotive Superintendent of the Tuleda & Bilbao Railway.

The elevation from the drawing office to the Works Managership gave Frank the opportunity to get involved in production matters at a critical time in the development of Crewe works as they were expanded to cope with the increasing demands placed upon the site. The layout of the works was still very much as it had been from the early days and Ramsbottom began to plan for a big increase in workload he sensed was coming, for the Board of the LNWR were beginning to consider combining all the building and repair of locomotives onto one site, this site being Crewe. The first priority was to make room for more repair and erecting facilities, a job started as Frank took office. The coach shop had already been transferred to Saltley and now the old wagon shop which had served as a general machining and wheel work facility was moved out, both these shops being turned over to locomotive erecting. By the time that these early changes had been made, in 1862, the Board decided to transfer all the Wolverton new locomotive building to Crewe, to be followed by all the repairs formerly carried out at that site.

With all this expansion and alteration, Frank was busy from his first day in office. In particular, the arrival of Wolverton-built engines placed an additional strain on the facilities. Not only were these engines of a completely different type, but they needed different techniques and tooling to handle their servicing. To this end some 400 Wolverton workmen were transferred to Crewe, together with their families, upping the town's population by some 1,700 persons at a stroke. These imports had to be housed, trained in Crewe methods and integrated into a large workforce. Amongst these new workers was a young George Whale, who was to become a rising star in future years, eventually to succeed Webb as Chief Mechanical Engineer (CME).

The reorganization of locomotive production onto one site was now beginning to take shape and the job of Works Manager was to be a key position in the overseeing of the massive changes and additions planned by Ramsbottom. Many of these were improvements crucial to the easement of the shifting of heavy loads around crowded shop floors. A rope-driven crane had been installed in the erecting shop created from the old wagon shops, and proved so beneficial that in 1862 more overhead traversing rope cranes had been installed in the main erecting shop, each of 20/25 tons capacity. By modern standards they may have been slow (80 ft/min. travelling speed and lifting speed of 9 ft/min.), but with just two men per crane they coped with all of the heavy lifting previously carried out by fixed block and tackle equipment operated by groups of labourers.

The works from its earliest days had produced much of the iron needed for not only the locomotive production, but also the rails. Steel was still expensive and not easy to come by in large quantities, but elsewhere metallurgists were experimenting with alloying and radical production methods. The latter involved the Bessemer process which was to revolutionise steel production worldwide. The employment of steel had been tried in the late 1850s on the LNWR for both straight and cranked axles and tyres, using crucible-produced steel from Yorkshire. However, this was an expensive material and Ramsbottom felt that he could not recommend its wide scale use because of this. So, apart from some experimental casting of some horn-blocks for the 'DX' and 'Problem' classes with a steel mixture, little progress could be made in switching to the stronger, more hard-wearing and malleable steel.

The Bessemer process, by 1861, had been brought to a state whereby it was considered suitably developed for commercial requirements and, more importantly, the cost of steel produced this way approached that of iron. Ramsbottom, satisfied with the limited trials of steel, proposed its adoption for axles, tyres, boilers and rails, putting this forward to the Crewe Committee that advised the Board.

Meantime, Frank Webb was trying out a scheme of his own to see if the iron rails currently being produced could be topped with steel to increase their lives. The process he developed was successful and was patented. This was to be the first of many patents during his time on the railway. But first to one of the early exercises which were carried out in the works reordering - an exercise which was to have a profound effect upon Frank Webb's career path.

In February/March of 1863, the Crewe Committee agreed to the construction of a Bessemer plant capable of producing 1,000 tons of steel per month and the necessary licence agreement negotiated with Bessemer. The plant was built in a space measuring 272 feet by 106 feet and comprised a pair of twin converters of 24 tons total capacity, three furnaces, a cogging mill, steam hammer and the all-important blowing engine. This new plant, which was built north of the Chester line on the newly acquired land to the west of the existing plant, was to form the core of the new enlarged locomotive factory planned to cater for the total production and servicing needs of the LNWR locomotive fleet. Frank's job expanded into a large undertaking as this programme took shape and the new plant was being planned. But he was more than capable of this quantum leap in his responsibility, for, in less than 18 months after the decision to proceed with the steel plant, the first 'blow' was made to produce the first of many ingots of steel. Initial production was limited and the changeover to steel as a raw material slow as a result. Early records are not available, but it can be surmised that there were some problems. Not surprisingly, because of the radical new process involved in the Bessemer method. Also, Frank's salary was by now at £600 (*circa* £72,000 today) in recognition of his efforts in getting the steel plant up and running.

The presence of a steel plant on site with key items such as tyres, axles, boilers, valve motion and frame plates being made from its output kept production costs down, by saving the transport costs from remote steel works and the continual worry of having to negotiate acceptable prices with manufacturers. The molten steel could be cast into suitable ingots and taken directly for working in the appropriate shop. For instance, a set of six tyres of a 'DX' could be completed in a little over five hours from pouring the melt into the casting ladle, following a procedure devised by Webb. Here we see a sharp mind at work, as he assimilated the new techniques associated with working this new, to Crewe, material. So often current thinking about Victorian industrial methods tends to criticise them as slow and out-moded, but here is an example which would be fully up to today's standards.

During Webb's years as a rising star in the works, the carriage construction had been progressively moved to Saltley, Birmingham, where a small factory had been built by the LNWR. This gave more urgently needed space in the original triangle at Crewe containing the carriage works for locomotive construction. Starting in 1856, this transfer was a leisurely affair, not being fully completed until 1860. However, the wish to concentrate all locomotive building at Crewe meant that the Saltley factory could be closed and the carriage work carried out there transferred to Wolverton. This happened from 1862 and in 1865 Saltley was closed completely. Ramsbottom could now start implementing the major expansion he needed and, with Frank Webb as his right-hand man and Works Manager, launched into the first stages of what was to be a major enlargement exercise beyond the new steel plant.

In 1866, as his experience in the production of steel was being built up, Frank Webb made an extraordinary change in his career. He tendered his resignation in February and, after the statutory four months' notice, on the 30th June departed to become Manager of the Bolton Iron & Steel Company, which had had a Bessemer converter in use since 1860. His involvement in the planning and setting up and operation of the Crewe steel plant must have played a large part in this move. He was one of the very few men in Britain with considerable experience in the running of a commercial Bessemer plant and would have been incredibly useful to the owners of the Bolton company. His involvement had led to a great interest in steel production and most certainly at Bolton he would have gained a great amount of experience for use later on. Matters at Crewe were such that future promotion prospects were restricted by the seemingly long period of time that Ramsbottom could be expected to stay in office, some 10 to 15 years being feasible.

It has been suggested that the Bolton job had been engineered by the LNWR management, Moon in particular, so that Frank could gain much additional experience of steel manufacture. This would answer the often asked question as to how he could walk back into the job at Crewe without any other contender being considered. However, the facts cannot be qualified and must remain as speculation.

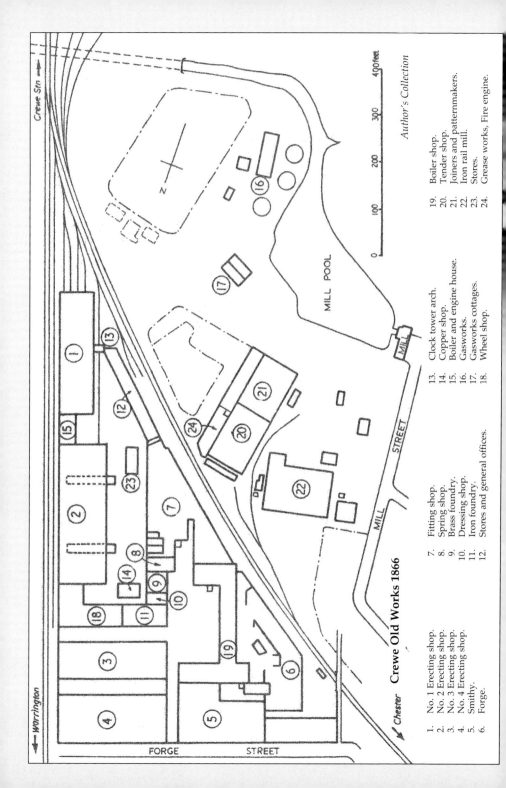

← Warrington

← Chester **Crewe Old Works 1866**

Author's Collection

Crewe Stn →

FORGE STREET

MILL STREET

MILL POOL

MILL

N

0   100   200   300   400feet

1. No. 1 Erecting shop.
2. No. 2 Erecting shop.
3. No. 3 Erecting shop.
4. No. 4 Erecting shop.
5. Smithy.
6. Forge.

7. Fitting shop.
8. Spring shop.
9. Brass foundry.
10. Dressing shop.
11. Iron foundry.
12. Stores and general offices.

13. Clock tower arch.
14. Copper shop.
15. Boiler and engine house.
16. Gasworks.
17. Gasworks cottages.
18. Wheel shop.

19. Boiler shop.
20. Tender shop.
21. Joiners and patternmakers.
22. Iron rail mill.
23. Stores.
24. Grease works, Fire engine.

Frank was very ambitious, and so long as he had uninhibited opportunities to apply his expertise, he was happy. Also, as far as Patents were concerned, the LNWR paid no royalties for the use of inventions created by their employees and maybe he felt that this was a bit on the unfair side. One of his inventions in the early 1860s was the curvilinear slotting machine for machining the inside of the rim of a wrought-iron wheel centre and it is significant that Ramsbottom recognised this and the steel-headed rail in particular as being worthy of note, mentioning this to the Locomotive Committee just before Webb departed for Bolton, viz:

> The Committee concur in Mr Ramsbottom's suggestion that a gratuity be presented to Mr Webb, being partly in recognition of the curved-surface shaping machine and the steel-headed rail both of which inventions, as Mr Ramsbottom informs them, are due to him, and they recommend that the sum of £500 [£60,000 today] be presented to Mr Webb...

This was duly approved, with the rider that the LNWR could use such of Webb's inventions then in use free of charge in the future. Parsimonious maybe, but when Webb was to return to the LNWR his salary was eventually such that it could be construed that there was a gentleman's agreement to compensate for all future inventions patented by him.

Ramsbottom was sorry to lose a competent Works Manager, but it has been speculated that this move of Webb's was looked upon as an opportunity for him to gather considerable experience in the techniques that lay behind the manufacture of different grades of steel, for it appears that little effort was made to dissuade him. However, it does seem plausible that Ramsbottom, who had a very high opinion of, and always got on well with Frank, may well have hinted that so far as his successor was concerned it probably would be Webb. Steel manufacture was set to become an integral part of Crewe works until finally shutdown in 1932.

A steam hammer in the forge in the Old Works.   E. Talbot Collection

Chapter Three

The Return to Crewe

Little is known of the years Webb spent at Bolton, but clearly he obtained great experience in running a large steelworks and doubtless absorbed many of the intricacies of dealing with the alloying processes which were to give steel its unique place in manufacturing industries. There is, however, one particular fact associated with this time; Webb's experience gained at Bolton gave him a good insight into the ways of working steel. It was during his days here that he thought up and obtained a patent, No. 3403, for a cast-steel locomotive frame block incorporating stretchers, horn-blocks and brackets. This was quite a revolutionary proposal, so revolutionary in fact that the idea was not taken up until the 1920s, when it was employed in the USA.

In 1867, Frank's youngest brother, William, graduated from Trinity College, Cambridge with BA and MA degrees and obtained a position of Assistant Curate at nearby Wigan's parish church, where his elder brother Arthur was a Curate. So, for a brief time, three of the four Webb boys were close together.

Back at Crewe the continuing expansion of the works was placing an ever greater workload on Ramsbottom, who was now approaching 57 years of age, and brought with it a breakdown in health for that capable engineer. So much so, that by September 1870 he gave in the 12 months' notice of his retirement, following which the existing Works Manager, Stubbs, died suddenly after a three-week illness. He had been a very competent manager, having been placed in that post from his chief draughtsman's position at the age of 30 by Ramsbottom, who had clearly recognised his potential. The position of Works Manager was filled temporarily by H.W. Kampf, who retained his chief draughtsman's position, whilst the Board began to think about a new Locomotive Superintendent.

It was the Chairman, Richard Moon, who made the first move, in contacting Webb at Bolton, to see if he was willing to return to Crewe. An interview took place following which Moon wrote to Webb:

> I took the opportunity as agreed of naming to our Special Committee what had passed with reference to your [possible] rejoining our Company as Locomotive Superintendent.
>
> 1st that the salary agreed should be £2,000 [c.£240,000 now] for the 1st year and £3,000 [c.£360,000] afterwards. We thought that the notice had best be as in the case of Mr Ramsbottom, twelve months, and that the number of pupils if you take any, for your own comfort as well as ours, should be limited to four.
>
> You know the regulations of the Company as to patents and other matters, so that I need not trouble you with them here.
>
> I do not know what rent Mr Ramsbottom pays for his house (Chester Place) but you can have it on the same terms as he has had it.
>
> I mentioned to the Committee that you could not leave the friends with whom you are at present for about 6 months, but that you may possibly arrange to leave them at an earlier period. We shall be ready for you whenever you can make arrangements to join us, and perhaps you will let me know after seeing your friends.

The Special Committee unanimously agreed to my proposal, and Mr Chance, the Chairman of the Locomotive Committee desired me to say that it has his special concurrence.
Hoping that you may have a long and promising career.

Correspondence continued between Moon and Webb, resulting in the agreement that Webb should finish at Bolton on 30th June, 1871 to rejoin the LNWR. The way was set for a recommencement of his railway career, yet another advancement brought about by unforeseen circumstances. Moon's approach to Webb leading to his return to Crewe was notable in that it appeared that all details had been agreed some time ago.

Moon's choice of Frank Webb for the new Locomotive Superintendent was also unique in that no other person seems to have been considered. This fact alone must have given Frank a great boost as to his absolute position and added to his opinion of his abilities. The energy, industrial and management skills of Webb made him a man fully fitting Moon's ambitions for the LNWR. Having given Frank a more or less free hand in his affairs, it was natural that his influence was to be such that few, if any, would question his orders. However, Webb was an autocrat and very individual in his engineering decisions. The stage was set for a few untoward events, which will be recounted later.

Moon, who had been Chairman for 10 years now, realised that here was a very competent engineer whom it was worth paying a generous starting salary with the implication that there could be more in the future. His backing of Ramsbottom had brought about a tremendous workload and, although it was said this led to a breakdown in health, however, other evidence suggests that Ramsbottom was dissatisfied with his remuneration. This despite the fact that his salary had advanced to £5,000 [c.£600,000] by 1869, truly a magnificent amount by the standards of the day, so the £2,000 offered to Webb was a sizeable saving in the salaries bill.

One feature of Moon's Chairmanship was that he ensured that the finance was available for the big increases in Ramsbottom and Webb's salaries, for he recognised that men of exceptional ability were worth big money. He also extended this to salary increases, on a much smaller scale, for the subordinates if this should be proposed by the Locomotive Superintendent.

Both Ramsbottom and Webb were keen on ordered management and sensible economics which agreed well with Moon's philosophy, though the economic feature was to have a dramatic effect on the size of locomotives in Moon's time. Webb's love of organization was echoed by Moon which made the rapport between them a pleasant feature and must have smoothed many an argument into agreement. He was also approachable by those in whom he believed to be promising, as witness his great interest in many of his outstanding pupils, two of whom, John Aspinall and Henry Ivatt, he had inherited from Ramsbottom.

However, with Frank having left Bolton in June and not actually scheduled to start at Crewe until the 1st October, there was a gap to be filled. This was catered for by a suggestion from Moon that he took, at LNWR expense, a short tour of the USA to study their steel-making and locomotive practices. The delay in starting was due to the fact that Ramsbottom had recovered somewhat from his illness now that he realised that the pressure would be off him very soon. So Frank sailed across the Atlantic to make his tour. One of the plants visited was that of the

Pennsylvania Railroad at Altoona. Here he looked up T.W. Worsdell, a previous acquaintance from his drawing office days at Crewe. They clearly had been good friends in those earlier days and Frank obviously had let it be known that he would be looking for a new Works Manager, for by the time he departed from Altoona Worsdell had written off to Crewe to apply for that position. He eventually got it but had to wait until November 1871 for confirmation. Frank knew he could rely on a competent Worsdell and had probably indicated this to the Board when fully established after Ramsbottom had gone.

Some of the American locomotive works had a profound effect upon Frank. He found them tidy and clean and very much involved in the production of standard parts applicable to a range of locomotive types. He immediately saw the merit in the mass production of such parts, it led to low costs which he knew was an important feature to Moon. We shall see how this concept of standardization, already established to a degree at Crewe by Trevithick, was to be rooted firmly by Frank in order to drive down unit costs. Not only did this technique assist in production costs, but in employing common methods of manufacture it held down the expense of providing extra tooling. Moon's suggestion of this visit to the USA was to pay vast dividends in the future. One classic example was the manufacture of express locomotive axle boxes one eighth of an inch smaller than those for goods locomotives, so that when the former were worn they could be bored out and used again on the latter.

Webb moved into the Crewe Locomotive Superintendent's house, Chester Place, as soon as Ramsbottom had vacated it. Here he was to stay for the following 32 years with just two or three domestics to manage the household affairs for him. The house was handy for access to the works, lying between the old works and steel works with the deviation works opposite. Within a few years the new office block was to be built, literally a stone's throw away, so getting to the office was only a couple of minutes walk. The grounds of Chester Place were quite extensive, which awakened a lasting interest in horticulture, with Webb spending some of his spare time meticulously tending the shrubs and flower beds. Gardening became an important recreation for him throughout much of his life. This hobby had been nurtured by his father who was a keen gardener and could be found in the early hours of the mornings in the Rectory garden tending his wide range of plants. The garden itself was an immaculate perfection of neatness and colour, a great example of excellent care. The children had been encouraged to take an interest in matters horticultural and this had clearly rubbed off on Frank in particular.

The workload at Crewe from 1871 was prodigious as the further expansion of the works proceeded apace. Ramsbottom had doubled its size in 10 years (1861-71) to make it the largest railway manufactory in the country at that time, but there was more to come. Webb and Worsdell spent much time planning and organizing this, with Frank making much of the running. Practically every suggestion or idea offered to him, and accepted, if it was eventually patented, was subtly modified to make it a Webb idea - he was a great one for keeping costs down, and no royalties were payable if it was an LNWR employee's idea. Yet there was another side to him, in connection with the introduction of new ideas, as in the instance of the Joy valve gear, which we shall see later.

Chester Place, the Locomotive Superintendent's house, which was used by Ramsbottom, Webb, Whale, Bowen-Cooke and Beames.

One immediate task was to deal with an order on Beyer, Peacock for sixteen 4-4-0Ts to their standard design supplied to other underground railways in London. The locomotives were required for suburban services around London, mainly on the North London and Outer Circle lines and, accordingly, were fitted with condensing gear. He let this order stand as his mind was fully engaged in getting to grips with his new position. The LNWR had never, except in the very early days of its now defunct Southern Division, placed orders for locomotives with an outside contractor. Once this one had been fulfilled, it was never to do so again until the pressures of wartime caused an order for 20 'Prince of Wales' 4-6-0s to be placed with North British Locomotive Co. in 1915. He was also highly critical of these 'foreign' products from the beginning and this came to a head in November 1873 during a discussion of a paper entitled *On Modern Locomotives* given by John Robinson at the Institution of Civil Engineers (ICE). The paper had attracted a clutch of notable locomotive engineers, namely Sir John Fowler, William Stroudley, Patrick Stirling and William Adams in addition to Frank Webb.

Webb's main criticisms of the Beyer, Peacock product was that it was heavy, had limited power and that he could design a 30 ton (the design weighed 47 tons) six-coupled tank which would do the job required of the 4-4-0T better. This produced some further discussion in which Webb was backed up by Stroudley who confirmed that a small six-coupled tank should be able to cope with trains of similar weight to those hauled by the Beyer, Peacock tanks, quoting some confirming statistics for his first batch of 'Terriers' which only weighed 24 tons.

4-4-0T 'Metropolitan' tank No. 3090 with condensing gear.   *John Alsop Collection*

Ramsbottom 2-4-0 'Newton' class No. 1745 *John Bright*.   *John Alsop Collection*

One feature of the 4-4-0 tanks which Frank criticised was the grate area, which for the underground use was larger than that for surface use. As most of the running over the LNWR routes was above ground he felt that the large grates were uneconomic and had firebricks put at the front end to try and reduce coal consumption.

Before going much further it will be helpful to consider the general layout of the Crewe works. There were three main areas, the old works, the deviation works and the steel works, The first-named comprised the original site and buildings of the GJR shops and sheds, the second an expansion of the former put up in the area between the old and new, or deviation, Chester lines, whilst the last was so-named as this was where the initial new steel plant was placed before the expansion of facilities under Webb. The expansion was limited to the west, by the Chester line, due to the northern, or more logical, expansion being blocked by housing developments which had grown up as the old works were being established.

With his steel experience, Webb immediately had the ears of Moon in ensuring that this more expensive, but long-lasting, material should be used to a greater extent in locomotives, for the employment of steel in place of iron had quite an impact on the life of parts. For instance, a steel driving wheel axle on a 2-2-2 'Problem' class was capable of running 158,000 miles before needing attention. This compared to the 74,000 miles for a wrought-iron axle. Once facts like this had been demonstrated Webb had little difficulty in obtaining Board approval for the funding further to expand the steel plant sufficiently to make Crewe self-sufficient in the supply of its needs. This did not make the LNWR very popular with the steel industry, but there was little they could do about the situation.

Between 1871 and 1874, the main task Moon had set himself was to promote the merger of the LNWR and the Lancashire & Yorkshire Railway (L&YR). This merger was proposed several times in those years, but each time it was set before the Parliamentary Committee it was thrown out, despite Moon's continued anticipation to the contrary.

As part of the early discussions between the Boards of the companies, it was decided to let Crewe build locomotives for the L&YR, that railway's Miles Platting works being inadequate to supply its needs. Additionally, the use of common types would be beneficial for the intended merger. The conviction of a successful outcome had led Moon to permit Crewe to commence supplying locomotives to the L&YR, in order to bring about common standards between the two railways.

Within a month of returning to Crewe, Frank was ordered to let the L&YR have six 'DX' 0-6-0s just completed and to build a further 20 for that line immediately. Shortly after, five 0-4-0Ts were to be transferred to the L&YR and five replacements built.

The sudden increase in production called for a considerable amount of overtime and extra machinery to be installed. As some key processes could not absorb this jump in productivity, the coppersmiths being a case in point, extra men had to be employed. The works manning having been dealt with, production for the L&YR continued and a further 40 'DX' plus 10 'Newton' class

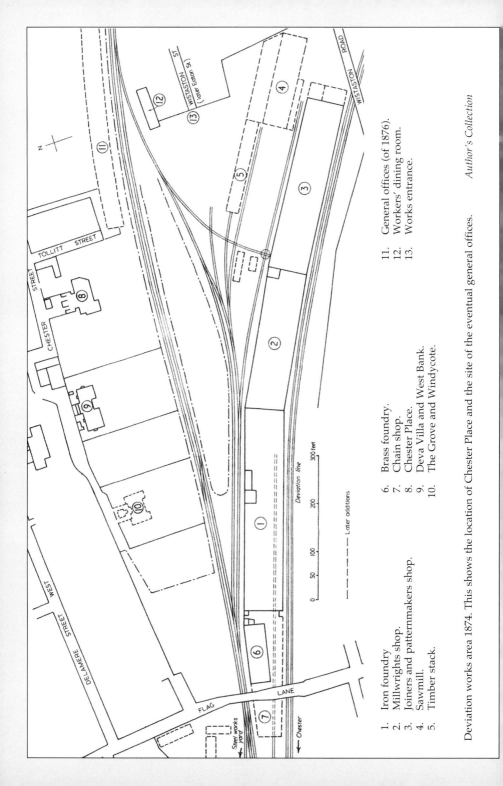

1. Iron foundry
2. Millwrights shop.
3. Joiners and patternmakers shop.
4. Sawmill.
5. Timber stack.

6. Brass foundry.
7. Chain shop.
8. Chester Place.
9. Deva Villa and West Bank.
10. The Grove and Windycote.

11. General offices (of 1876).
12. Workers' dining room.
13. Works entrance.

Deviation works area 1874. This shows the location of Chester Place and the site of the eventual general offices.

Author's Collection

2-4-0s were supplied. Matters proceeded through to 1875, by which time some 86 'DXs', 10 2-4-0s and five 0-4-0Ts had been supplied to the L&YR at a cost of £225,000.

This programme of supply remained in place until an outside private builder of locomotives, in the shape of the Yorkshire Engine Company, got to hear of this competition to its business. At the instigation of A.L. Sacré, manager of that concern, the Locomotive Manufacturers Association was formed and succeeded in getting a court injunction which prevented the LNWR building locomotives for any other railway. This injunction held, for by this time it was clear that a merger was not on the cards. It also, by inference, applied to all the railway companies in Britain and was to last until the formation of British Railways, when it became irrelevant. Only once was this ruling overturned, in World War II, when the LMS '8F' 2-8-0 was built by other railway companies, ostensibly for their own use. Some of those constructed were eventually to find their way onto the LMS lines but, by then, Nationalisation loomed.

Also, as we have seen above, the setting up of a big steel plant aggrieved the steel industry. The LNWR was becoming a fully self-contained entity according to Moon's plans and Webb was fast becoming an important player in these.

One little feature of design which can be attributed to Webb was the arrival of the cab on the LNWR locomotives to replace the rather sparse weather-boards of his predecessors. This was an early modification first appearing in 1872.

One feature which Frank found added to the LNWR inventory was the provision of water troughs on many of the main lines. Ramsbottom had designed the apparatus capable of picking up water at speed and was having it fitted to many locomotives. Moon had approved the expenditure on this as he saw that the laying down of water troughs and the fitting of locomotives with the pick-up gear offered benefits. He could see the potential of speeding up services by eliminating lengthy stops to take on water, and in addition the tender size could be kept down. This latter fact was to become a feature of LNWR locomotives for many years to come. Smaller tenders took less time to construct and could still be made with wooden underframes, both features which kept costs down. With express train weights of less than 80 tons at that time, if some 1,200 gallons of water were not carried this represented well over 6 per cent of the load hauled and would thereby offer a small reduction in fuel consumed, yet another argument for the ability to pick up water on the move.

32   F.W. WEBB : IN THE RIGHT PLACE AT THE RIGHT TIME

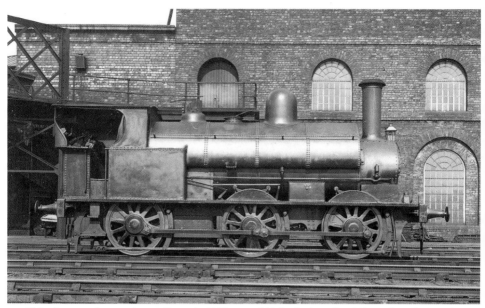

This photograph was taken at Crewe in 1933, so could it be the long-lived 'Special' tank No. 3323 works shunter?

MRT/R.G. Jarvis Collection

One of the 0-6-0T 'Special' tank works shunters at Wolverton carriage works in 1933.

MRT/R.G. Jarvis Collection

Chapter Four

Consolidation at Crewe

Frank Webb's early days at Crewe as Locomotive Superintendent were full of several other extraneous matters affecting his already heavy workload. One such matter, running concurrently with the L&YR episode described earlier, was that the price of coal more than doubled, from 7s. 0d. [£37] per ton in 1871 to 15s. 0d. [£90] a ton in 1874. The effect of this, not only on the locomotive department but on the production side, was to increase the running costs of the LNWR considerably. As a matter of interest, out of the total weights of materials required for the construction of a typical locomotive, some 41 per cent was attributed to the coal required for the many processes involved. This may seem a large percentage but this coal did not go through any added-value processing, it was consumed in the processes needed for raw materials to be turned into the end product. The net effect on the final cost of a locomotive was, therefore, relatively small.

However, this price increase only proved temporary, for by 1876 it had fallen back to 8s. 0d. [£48] a ton and was eventually to regain its old cost of 7s. 0d. by 1879. (Nowadays, one can be expected to pay £100-120 a ton for good steam coal.) This experience had planted a seed in Webb's mind, for he was very cost-conscious, and was to lead into his future adoption of compounding.

The root cause of the shift in coal price was the economic depression sweeping through Britain, which peaked in 1874 and then slowly subsided back to normality. This gave Webb an extra incentive to keep costs to an acceptable level, so it was not surprising that so much effort and time was spent on refining the works equipment and procedures to achieve that.

The works reorganization was combined with the expansion programme and had, under Webb, a dramatic effect on the number of locomotives awaiting or undergoing repairs. In the 1860s under Ramsbottom it had not been uncommon to have 19-20 per cent of the entire LNWR stock at Crewe for that purpose. This was clearly uneconomic and Frank was determined to try and do something about this. He and Worsdell took stock of the situation and began to replace outdated machine tools with new and better examples. They also introduced some revised working procedures to eliminate time wasting and saw to it that new foundries, forges, machine shops, etc. were provided at strategic locations in the expanding works. Some components would need to travel over a mile from a machine shop to the point where they were needed on the production line, so timing of delivery could be crucial, such was the size of the works by now. Both Webb and Worsdell were sticklers for discipline and the strict control of the workforce by the foremen, many of whom were Public School products and reckoned as such to be capable of imparting such requirements. Commensurate with the LNWR Board's thinking of gentlemanly conduct of those in key positions, several foremen had received their education at none other than Eton itself.

So far as the works layout was concerned, there were some areas which tended to be largely unaffected, as witness the erecting shop's spare space full

Molten metal being poured into moulds in the iron foundry.　　　　　*E. Talbot Collection*

Crewe works boiler shop. A boiler is in position in the riveting tower and the apparatus on the right is a punch for making holes in plate.　　　　　*E. Talbot Collection*

of machines such as wheel lathes, slotters, cylinder borers and planers. The 'fitting' shop was really a machine shop, 'a perfect maze of pulleys, straps, shafts and revolving wheels' as Bowen Cooke put it in later years. The expansion of the steel plant area should have given the opportunity to redress the crowded state so far as the fitting shop was concerned, but this had to wait until 1903 when a dedicated building was erected to provide a main machine shop alongside the new No. 9 erecting shop. Most other railway works nearly always had a separate fitting shop area, but Crewe did not, preferring to combine the smaller machining tasks and fitting tasks into one area. Why Webb did not separate the disciplines is a mystery, perhaps because that is the way it was during his time as Works Manager, combined with the need for cost control impressed upon him, that coloured his thinking. After all, it served the production needs competently and the argument for reorganizing matters never got much support until very much later, although doubtless the men employed would have gladly welcomed a more spacious environment.

When Webb took over the Locomotive Superintendency, the working week at Crewe was 58 hours, by no means the longest in the country, but already a bone of contention. Throughout the industrial concerns of the country there was a general movement for a nine-hour working day which was growing in strength. Such trades unions as existed were in their infancy and had little or no influence at that time; their days were to come in the 20th century. Wishing to placate a clearly determined workforce and realising that some concession would make his reforms easier to implement, Frank obtained permission to bring in a 54 hour working week. This commenced on 1st January, 1872 and was notable for the way in which the works activities were altered to maintain production levels without any increase in the workforce. This indicates the grasp that both Webb and Worsdell had of working practices at Crewe and Webb, in particular, was to take an unremitting interest on an almost daily basis. The 58 hour week would have had to be reduced in 1875 to 56 hours anyway, due to the Factory Act of that year. Whether or not Webb had any forewarning of this Act is not known, but in any case, the LNWR, by overshooting the proposal of the Act, certainly fortuitously played a trump card well ahead of this legislative change.

Having gained some success in bringing about the reduction in working hours the next request from the shop floor, after a few months of settling into the new routines, was for a pay rise. This, however, was not forthcoming except for limited success in a few areas.

With his locomotive designs, Frank began cautiously by keeping the Ramsbottom 2-4-0s of the 'Samson' and 'Newton' classes in production for express work. His first complete design, an 0-6-0, was based very much on his involvement on the 'DX'. The new 0-6-0, or 'Coal Engine' as it became known, appeared in 1873 to supersede the 'DX', still being turned out up to the end of 1872. Production of this latter class eventually totalled 943 including the 86 for the L&YR.

Concurrent with the new 'Coal Engine' some new 2-4-0s, of two classes, began to be out-shopped in 1874. These were the 'Precursor' and 'Precedent' classes, the former class eventually totalling 40 and the latter 70. The

Crewe works, the machine shop. *Author's Collection*

A slightly more orderly group of machine tools in the steel works. *Author's Collection*

'Newton' class 2-4-0 No. 1482 *Herschel* at Manchester (London Road). *John Alsop Collection*

'Newton' class No. 1666 *Ariadne* caught at Birmingham (New Street) in August 1903.
R.S. Carpenter Collection

0-6-0 '17 in. Coal Engine' No. 433 at Heaton Chapel.   *John Alsop Collection*

0-6-0 'Coal Engine' No. 2153, erected in 25½ hours, with the gangs involved. The tall young clean-shaven man between the two bearded characters on the left is C.J. Bowen-Cooke.

Author's Collection

0-6-0 '17 in. Coal Engine' No. 2097.   *John Alsop Collection*

'Precursor' had 5 ft 6 in. driving wheels and had been derived from an experience during Frank's time in the USA. This was that he had noticed on the Pennsylvania Railroad that 4-4-0s with 5 ft 6 in. wheels were used quite extensively on express work in hilly areas. This clearly had impressed him and he had resolved to adopt this principle. On his accession to the top job at Crewe, he had taken a McConnell fast goods 0-6-0, which had this wheel diameter, converted it to a 2-4-0 and tried it out on express work. This proved successful and was used as a rôle model for the 'Precursor'. The 'Precedent' was a logical development having larger (6 ft 6 in.) driving wheels.

Robust and reliable locomotives, they were put into service on the main line express and passenger services throughout the LNWR. Although they eventually became rather small when compared to other railways' designs for similar duties in later years, they coped well with the train weights and speeds of the day. Moon still pressed home his cost minimisation policy and flatly refused to consider approving any tender locomotives with more that six wheels or axle loads over 15 tons. This policy somewhat constrained Webb's designs, but at least with the new sturdy steel boilers they could be driven hard without too much ill-effect.

So much criticism has been aimed at the Midland Railway (MR) and its small engine policy that the LNWR's similar leanings have tended to be put on one side. Webb locomotives most certainly were 'lightweights', at least while Moon was Chairman, but in terms of power per unit weight they were definitely amongst the best - at least the simples and most of the compounds.

From 1873 Webb introduced the famous 'Blackberry Black' with lining for all except goods and most shunting engines. To paint a locomotive took one month, in 19 separate stages. The result of this meticulous approach gave a high-quality finish which would last the time between general repairs and was said to cost more than the assembly in the erecting shop, it being a very labour-intensive job. No modern mixing and blending and spray painting by robots as today, hand preparation, application and finishing was the norm.

2-4-0 'Precursor' class No. 402 *Viscount* at Chester.   *John Alsop Collection*

2-4-0 'Precursor' class No. 847 *Cedric* at Chester.   *John Alsop Collection*

'Precedent' class 2-4-0 No. 955 *Charles Dickens* which ran 1 million miles in 9 years and 219 days and by 1902 had amassed a total of 2 million miles. *Author's Collection*

'Precedent' class 2-4-0 No. 2191 *Snowdon*. *John Alsop Collection*

The braking of trains was a subject over which much deliberation was beginning to be taken throughout Britain. It had, for many years, been quite commonplace for tender engines to rely on tender brakes plus, for emergencies, the reversing of the driven wheels, an act which must have produced great wear on both tyres and rails. Ramsbottom had taken note of the Clarke chain brake as a possible means of introducing semi-continuous braking to a train. This device did, however, need some action by both the engine crew and the guard for correct operation. Before Frank returned to the LNWR it had been decided that the Clarke system was to be adopted. In 1872 an early version of the Westinghouse air brake had been tested by the LNWR but rejected because of the cost. However, in later years, George Westinghouse managed to get an appointment to see Webb at Crewe and promote his improved braking system. He did get as far as getting some move to a tentative agreement for his invention to be put forward as the preferred system but unfortunately hinted that Webb would benefit from a substantial commission, which was standard American business practice. Frank unfortunately saw in this more than a hint of bribery, which was not at all gentlemanly, and terminated the, up to then, cordial discussion and asked Westinghouse to leave. By this time the Clarke-Webb chain brake had been designed and patented, based on the original Clarke system, demonstrated at the Newark Brake Trials and was to be adopted by the LNWR as its standard. This despite the fact that the first of these trials resulted in the LNWR train parting into two portions! However, some speedy repairs under the guidance of Worsdell, who had been delegated by Webb to oversee the trials, resulted in satisfactory operation thereafter with some very good stops being demonstrated. For more details of the chain brake see Chapter Six.

So Westinghouse had, it seems, been on a fruitless mission, for to change horses in mid stream would have been seen by Moon as a waste of money. This would also have put Webb in an awkward position, quite probably he realised this and was only too glad to find an excuse to terminate any further considerations. After all, it was hoped that other railways might adopt the Clarke-Webb system to the benefit of the LNWR and Webb himself. But in the event this never materialised, for in the background lurked the Board of Trade which had the weight of Government legislative procedures behind it.

As far as brakes were concerned, Moon was violently opposed to anything promoted by Government bodies. His opinion of organizations such as the Board of Trade was not very high, even though so much railway legislation emanated from that body. This appears to be why, despite Webb's leanings towards a vacuum system, much was made of the Clarke-Webb device - it was an in-house development and could be manufactured at the LNWR plants and, of course, no royalties would be payable.

Frank was perceptive enough to realise Moon's bias and ensured that he made the Clarke-Webb system as reliable as possible. In fact, for the early years of its use it was remarkably free of trouble in operation, and certainly as effective as the simple vacuum system then being gradually adopted by some of the other railways, the London, Brighton & South Coast, Great Eastern, Caledonian and North British having opted for the Westinghouse air brake.

On 27th June, 1873, the Shah of Persia visited Crewe works, arriving by special train, which apparently was hauled by 'Problem' 2-2-2 No. 806 *Waverley*. This was one of the first of this class to be modified by Webb by the fitting of his style of chimney and a cab. For this auspicious occasion the locomotive was temporarily renamed *Shah of Persia* in Persian script and carried a symbolic crown between the chimney and dome. It was also specially painted in the new LNWR lined black livery which became standard thereafter. Frank was on hand to assist in the tour of the works and answer any questions. This tour was marked by the effect on the Shah of a demonstration of a circular saw for cutting hot metal ingots, recently transferred from the old works. The saw itself was an impressive 7 feet in diameter with blades than ran at 13,000 feet per minute and when put into operation, the eminent dignitary was somewhat taken aback by the noise and shower of sparks produced.

Running concurrently with the braking story, yet another engineering task had landed on Webb's desk in 1873. This was an order to set up a signalling department 'to undertake the manufacture of signal and locking apparatus as well as points and crossings'. As usual, this emanated from Moon's cost reduction programme, for he had realised that an efficient signalling programme should help somewhat, by employing fewer staff and enabling better control of train movements. Up to this point in time, much of the signalling work had been contracted out to the specialist firm of Saxby and Farmer. The relevant agreement covering this work was by now approaching renewal, but Moon had decided to let it lapse, as in his continual drive to reduce operating costs he felt that in-house manufacture and maintenance would be cheaper. Accordingly, on learning that the LNWR was considering taking the signalling under its wing, Saxby & Farmer, whilst they could not see their way to reducing their charges and clearly wishing to maintain the status quo, pointed out that many patents were in existence on their equipment which the railway might well infringe. Moon, realising that in Webb he had a man well versed in patent matters and always ready to find a way round them, persisted in his plan. Frank was ordered to investigate and report on what would be needed at Crewe to accomplish the task specified.

Moon began by head-hunting an experienced man. He found him employed by Saxby & Farmer, in the form of one George Edwards, who was enticed away from a steady job to the position of Signal Engineer for the LNWR. Edwards began by liasing with Frank Webb, who picked his brains about the intricacies of the Saxby & Farmer equipment in order to circumvent the patents' position.

The adoption of in-house production of signalling equipment was a major step for the LNWR to take and Frank grasped it eagerly, for here was something new to him, and he loved the challenge that such opportunities offered. He speedily set up a core organization in his department for the design and manufacture of new and replacement signalling equipment, appointing J.S. Bean to take charge of that. Many of his patents around this time were to be in connection with this responsibility.

The expensive item in any signalling system was the interlocking frame, which underwent frequent use, particularly at busy junctions. The wear was considerable, so reliability and ease of maintenance were two design features which Webb impressed on the drawing office staff responsible for the detail design. One of these was his pupil H.A. Hoy, who had made several models of points and signals interlocking devices. His interest in such matters had been aroused following an accident at Wigan, for the enquiry into which he made a model of the track work involved. However, the first design produced under Frank for the interlocking system failed to pass the scrutiny of the Patent Office adjudicators. They ruled it still accomplished the locking in a similar method to that patented by Saxby. Even though it looked different, the underlying principle was too close to be acceptable for a new patent. Frank accordingly went back to the drawing board and designed yet another system of interlocking which passed the severe inspection of the Patent Office and became the model for all future signalling developments on the LNWR.

As a matter of interest, Edwards only remained with the LNWR for three years, leaving in 1876 to join the Gloucester Wagon Company when that organization decided to expand its services to cover signalling equipment. He then, in 1881, set up his own company the Railway Signal Co. which was to become one of the leading, if not *the* leading, signalling contractors towards the end of the 1800s. Clearly he still had a good rapport with Webb, for this latter company was to obtain a large number of contracts from the LNWR.

To assist in the supply of signal equipment the old tender shop in the old works was turned over to the new department as a production centre in 1874-75. The importance of the new department grew and, in 1877, Webb appointed Charles Dick, then chief draughtsman, as manager. Dick and Webb always got on well and the 'Precursors', 'Precedents' and 'Coal Engines' had been designed under Dick's leadership. The signal department manager's job was a particularly taxing one, involving much time out on the railway in what could be extreme weather conditions. Dick was not very robust and was probably glad when he received his next promotion in 1882 to the position of Works Manager to replace Worsdell who had gone to the Great Eastern Railway as Locomotive Superintendent. The signal work was eventually to cover over 1,500 signal boxes controlling about 17,000 signals, a big undertaking and responsibility indeed.

Later on, A.M. Thompson was appointed as Signal and Telegraph Superintendent, the two disciplines went together logically and Webb had developed, with the help of Thompson, an electro-mechanical method for signal operation, which became known as the Webb-Thompson system. The association with Thompson brought about one other episode of romance in Frank's life. Thompson had a daughter who caught his eye and he began to court her, to be thwarted by her father who, for some reason, considered the match to be inappropriate. To give Frank his due, this rebuff did not affect his relationship with Thompson, for he went on with that gentleman to patent many signalling improvements right up to 1902.

A further signalling development, to derive from Webb's interest in electrical matters, was his invention of the Electric Train Staff to provide a great safety feature on single line operation. This was patented and eventually was to be found in many countries of the world where single line operation was the norm.

Chapter Five

The Early Influences

Upon his accession to Locomotive Superintendent Webb took over Ramsbottom's pupils. Amongst these were two who, in years to come, would rise to the top on other railways, H.A. Ivatt and J.A.F. Aspinall. Both of these were already making their mark at Crewe and Aspinall, in particular, was noted for his keen attention to all the tasks to come his way. At the end of his pupilage Webb accordingly made him one of the Indoor Assistants or Deputies to Worsdell, the newly appointed Works Manager. Aspinall clearly settled well into this responsible position; so well that in early 1872 Frank arranged for him to be sent to the United States to view the latest railway and steel-making processes over there. Some letters of introduction from both Webb and Worsdell were provided to ease his path. Aspinall was not yet 21, so the experience gained was to be of considerable use in later years and his return to Crewe was enhanced by the insight into the American ways in industrial and technical expertise.

On his return from North America, Aspinall found Webb busy organizing a works tour for delegates from the Institution of Mechanical Engineers' Summer Meeting in August. The meeting was to be held in Liverpool that year, so the planning involved the provision of a special train to transport the delegates, many of them very influential and experienced engineers, plus an appropriate reception and conducted tour of Crewe works. Frank also made sure that Aspinall was to be one of the party around to answer relevant questions whilst he himself lead the tour. It seemed obvious that this young man was set for high places and that early experience of dealing with top professionals would be of great benefit to him.

This event went well with Frank personally conducting them around in style. He clearly was proud of the expanding facilities and was determined to show off the new layout which turned raw materials into a finished product on one site.

One little benefit noted by the young high-flyer Aspinall was that those such as himself certainly gained much experience from the early introduction to considerable responsibility. He was to adopt this principle in his own time as CME of the Great Southern & Western Railway (GSWR) and L&YR in later years.

At the end of 1872 Aspinall finished his pupilage, being rewarded by the appointment of Assistant Manager of the steel works, as the extension works were called.

As the works' expansion proceeded apace, Webb turned his mind to the mundane, but essential, task of sourcing the bricks required. For some years now Crewe had manufactured its own bricks on site, largely by hand, using clay taken from soil removed from cuttings near Crewe station. Excavations for the new shops had resulted in large quantities of suitable clay soil being dumped in fields nearby where the subsoil was also similar in nature. He reckoned that a considerable saving in the cost of bricks could be made by organizing the mechanisation of brick-making. Moon gladly provided a quite

John Aspinall, during his time as Locomotive Superintendent at Inchicore.   *Author's Collection*

modest capital amount, some £5,000, to set up a new brickworks on site and the first 11 months' output of this produced nearly 5 million bricks at 15s. [£83] per thousand. This delighted Moon in his constant search for processes to drive down costs, for the cost compared to 19s. [£105] per thousand for non-mechanised manufacture or even more for bought-out materials. At that rate of production and associated costs, Moon's investment would have been repaid in under five years.

John Aspinall, having been given total responsibility for this very successful programme, clearly had proved his competence to Webb, and was to be further encouraged by having his salary doubled, before being given ever more key responsibilities as the years progressed. Webb certainly recognised great ability when he saw it and, as Crewe had a reputation for guiding high-flyers into key posts, it was only a matter of time before Aspinall would be directed to a highly responsible job elsewhere if he could not be placed somewhere on the LNWR. In the event Aspinall moved to the GSWR in Ireland. Experience gained on another railway would always be very useful should that person return to Crewe higher up the ladder. We shall see that Aspinall might well have briefly considered such a move from the L&YR in later years as Webb's retirement approached, but was neatly diverted by the L&YR Board's decision to keep him by offering him the post of General Manager of that line. A complete list of those to be nurtured and picked out for such advancement is given in *Appendix One*.

The connection between Crewe works and the Inchicore works of the GSWR, then the largest engineering concern in Ireland, grew largely from the decision of the latter to install a steel rolling mill, the first to appear over there. This installation was based on that at Crewe, and Inchicore sent across a key foreman to be trained in its use. This clearly opened some dialogue between the hierarchy of the two works, for in 1876 Webb learned from Alexander McDonnell, the Locomotive Superintendent there, that a new Works Manager was needed at Inchicore. McDonnell was an old colleague of Frank, having worked under him at Crewe in years past. Casting his mind to the recent competent handling by Aspinall of all the tasks to come his way he called him to his office one day and mentioned this post in Ireland, adding the rider 'and I am recommending you'.

Another pupil of note taken over by Webb was H.A. Ivatt, a great friend of Aspinall, with whom he had served his apprenticeship. Ivatt was yet another very worthy youngster who showed a great practical side to his capabilities. Hence at the end of his pupilage he was retained and given a job in the Running Department, where he started as a fireman based at Crewe shed. This posting lasted six months, after which Webb saw to it that he was appointed assistant foreman at Stafford shed. A year passed and the clearly competent Ivatt found himself in charge at Holyhead for a couple of years before going on to Chester.

By 1877, not long after Aspinall had settled into the Works Managership at Inchicore, Ivatt, having achieved over three years' running experience under his belt, moved to Ireland. An opportunity on the GSWR, engineered by Aspinall, had materialised. This was the job of Southern District Division Superintendent based at Cork, and Webb was happy to endorse this appointment.

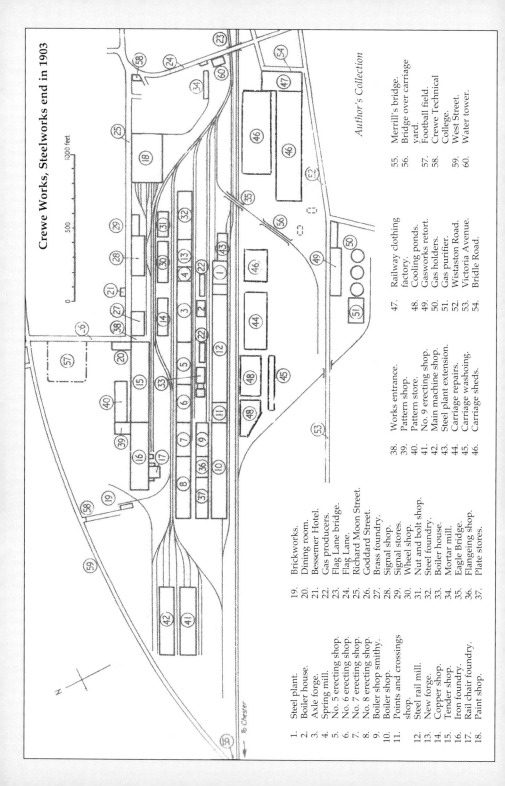

Crewe Works, Steelworks end in 1903

Author's Collection

1. Steel plant.
2. Boiler house.
3. Axle forge.
4. Spring mill.
5. No. 5 erecting shop.
6. No. 6 erecting shop.
7. No. 7 erecting shop.
8. No. 8 erecting shop.
9. Boiler shop smithy.
10. Boiler shop.
11. Points and crossings shop.
12. Steel rail mill.
13. New forge.
14. Copper shop.
15. Tender shop.
16. Iron foundry.
17. Rail chair foundry.
18. Paint shop.
19. Brickworks.
20. Dining room.
21. Bessemer Hotel.
22. Gas producers.
23. Flag Lane bridge.
24. Flag Lane.
25. Richard Moon Street.
26. Goddard Street.
27. Brass foundry.
28. Signal shop.
29. Signal stores.
30. Wheel shop.
31. Nut and bolt shop.
32. Steel foundry.
33. Boiler house.
34. Mortar mill.
35. Eagle Bridge.
36. Flangeing shop.
37. Plate stores.
38. Works entrance.
39. Pattern shop.
40. Pattern store.
41. No. 9 erecting shop.
42. Main machine shop.
43. Steel plant extension.
44. Carriage repairs.
45. Carriage washoing,
46. Carriage sheds.
47. Railway clothing factory.
48. Cooling ponds.
49. Gasworks retort.
50. Gas holders.
51. Gas purifier.
52. Wistaston Road.
53. Victoria Avenue.
54. Bridle Road.
55. Merrill's bridge.
56. Bridge over carriage yard.
57. Football field.
58. Crewe Technical College.
59. West Street.
60. Water tower.

Although Webb never had any recorded experience of footplate tasks, he, however, ensured that many of his pupils did obtain this important feature in their own training. The firing and driving of locomotives was, to some, a necessary skill to be experienced as they rose through the ranks, but Frank, although happy to disport himself on the footplates of his creations, was never recorded as getting his hands on the controls. When one further plea, for a good running man this time, emanated from Inchicore in 1877, Frank cast around for a suitable candidate, no doubt happy that many of his bright young men were being sent away as soon as he had trained them to spread the Crewe gospel. He selected H.A. Ivatt, by then in charge of the locomotive department at Chester. The Ivatt/Aspinall combination in Ireland was to become a classic time of improvements and advancement in the design and construction of locomotives at Inchicore.

Both Aspinall and Ivatt were to become successive Locomotive Superintendents at Inchicore before returning to the mainland and the L&YR and Great Northern Railway (GNR) Locomotive Superintendent's posts respectively. Throughout their stay in Ireland they often would call in at Crewe to seek advice from Webb, or merely talk over some technical matters then coming under their remit. Whilst Webb rarely condoned sharing his thoughts with engineers from other railways, he would always find time to mull things over with his old pupils, after all, it was largely through his wise advice and guidance that had led to the advancements possible elsewhere. Plus, of course, his own perception of their clear abilities which marked them out for quick promotion.

Contrasting with his meticulous handling of his pupils, Webb was very reluctant to accept ideas from others he considered to be of lesser ability. If any suggestion as to an alternative way of achieving some design aim was put his way, he would firmly reject, or even ignore, it. He did not want any diversion from his own ideas and clung stubbornly to the schemes as outlined by himself. Any outside suggestions or inventions he though suitable for consideration were subtly altered so that the LNWR escaped any royalties for adopting such improvements; about the only thing he adopted without tinkering with it was the Joy valve gear. He was to strike up a long-lasting friendship with David Joy and was very enthusiastic about the valve gear, which eliminated the need for eccentric drive and was thus economic to manufacture. This was the only outside invention for which the LNWR was to pay patent royalties during Webb's time. Joy was an enthusiastic inventor and this sort of person was close to Webb's heart, for he was recorded as referring to him as 'Dear old David Joy'. A fuller appraisal of this association is to be found in the next Chapter.

As the steelworks end of the Crewe works was being expanded under Frank's plans, the increase in staffing needed to cope with this resulted in the office accommodation alongside the clock tower in the old works becoming increasingly congested. These offices were also located away from the new works, inconvenient for those with responsibilities there and Frank himself, so a new office block was built facing the old Chester line and in 1876 much of the design and administration departments were moved into it. The new office premises were also conveniently placed close to Chester Place and other company houses

The drawing office, situated in the new office block.   *E. Talbot Collection*

and had Webb's office plus those of the chief clerk, Works Manager, the two running superintendents and two outdoor superintendents on the ground floor. The drawing office was also located at this level. The first floor contained the various accountant's offices, stores office, a laboratory and a photographic department. From here all the major affairs dealing with operation, output and all design matters at Crewe works were to be run for over 70 years.

In 1879 there occurred a significant event which showed Webb at his organizational best, in that it involved arranging the tasks of design and production in conjunction with major works carried out by the Civil Engineering Department. On the 17th August of that year a violent storm producing torrential rain swept across the Welsh mountains. Vast amounts of water burst many river banks and that flowing down the valley containing the Llandulas viaduct undermined the foundations. The viaduct collapsed and much was carried away by the rushing torrent. This viaduct carried the main line between Chester and Holyhead, and the important LNWR route to the Irish Sea ferries was cut. It took two days for the floods to subside before the Civil Engineer could begin some form of remedial action. The first task was to deviate the line over half a mile and erect a temporary trestle bridge across the river at its narrowest point. Exactly seven days after the collapse the first train passed over this diversion.

Meantime, back at Crewe, a new viaduct had been designed and Webb had the steelworks busy manufacturing and rolling the steel needed to produce the girders, plates and angles for the replacement structure. It was a huge undertaking, for the viaduct was to be 224 feet long divided into seven spans of 32 feet and had a maximum height of 50 feet. A total of 42 girders constructed from the components turned out by the steelworks were transhipped for erection on new piers and, by the 14th September, the viaduct was opened for traffic. The speed of construction was helped considerably by the use of electric lighting at night to enable 24 hour working. Webb was convinced of the merits of such methods of illumination and encouraged its application in this case in order to speed up the rebuilding process. The Chester-Holyhead line was a key one on the LNWR and every day of closure or restricted services ate into the returns.

The growth in mechanisation resulting from new engineering techniques in the mining industry had a significant effect on the output per miner in the couple of decades up to 1880. The output of coal per year rose from 110 million tons in 1870 to 160 million tons in 1883 (a 45 per cent increase), which ensured supplies of cheap coal enabling the British iron industry to outstrip the total iron production of the rest of the world. However, elsewhere in the world, other producers were also benefiting from the advances and the greater production available led to falling prices of the materials needed for iron and steel production. This latter fact ensured that some of the capital required for Crewe works expansion was available due to savings in the cost of raw materials.

With the railway's fortunes tending to follow the trend in industrial output, Webb was always engaged on a search for accurate and effective cost control. Moon, likewise, kept a watching brief over the performance of Crewe works, continually striving to balance the books so that a good dividend was paid to the shareholders who, thus far, had steadily supported the Board's handling of their investments. It is said that Moon had a large letter 'D' mounted prominently within his gaze in his office to remind him of the need to strive for an acceptable dividend. He was also frequently to be found at Crewe in conclave with Webb on matters concerning not only locomotives but many manufacturing aspects, particularly where capital expenditure was concerned. On some of these occasions his family (there were six children), would accompany him and be entertained at Chester Place. There was a report that Frank and one of Moon's daughters were getting quite close, but that the 'hereditary disease' fear put paid to that. However, this is only a speculative report and, as the 'disease' only surfaced towards the end of Frank's career, it seems quite possible that some irreverent back-dating of that rumour produced this comment. In fact, a more believable report mentions that a proposal was in fact offered, but rejected. Which daughter was involved has not surfaced.

The particular fact about Frank Webb's forebear's associations mentioned in Chapter One may seem a bit irrelevant but, on reflection, the author wonders if an inkling of this earlier generation's antics filtered down to Richard Moon, the LNWR Chairman, and thereby put a block on any deeper association of this daughter with Frank. Victorians were notoriously rigid in their interpretations of what was right and what was wrong. If that was the case, at least the grandfather's liaison did not affect Webb's position on the LNWR. Moon may have been dismayed at the Webb family's past history, but it certainly did not affect his support for a Locomotive Superintendent who was so capable at his job and produced precisely what was needed, motive power economic to run and cheap to build.

Rebuilt 'Samson', or Whitworth' class 2-4-0 No. 764 *Shap* at Carnforth on 22nd April, 1905.
John Alsop Collection

'Whitworth' class No. 36 *Thalaba* at Bletchley.   *John Alsop Collection*

Chapter Six

Onwards in Design

The period from 1876 to 1898 saw over 1,600 new locomotives emerge from Crewe works which were not compounds. Locomotives which were to be the backbone of many of the LNWR operations - local passenger, semi-fast passenger, local freight, long-distance freight, mixed traffic, down to the everyday tasks of shunting works, goods yards or docks and even crane engines - came into service to fulfil the needs for motive power provision.

The supplying of all these placed a heavy load on Frank Webb for the design of so many differing types in a relatively short time; particularly as he was very heavily committed to starting his compound developments, planning yet further expansions to the works in addition to an ever-growing involvement in local, and county, affairs coming his way. However, he was aided considerably by the adoption, wherever possible, of standard parts applicable to a large number of designs. This followed the similar philosophy he had seen during his visits to American railway workshops in 1871.

The investment needed was always at the top of the agenda and there were several ways in which this could be helped. The design aspect was considerably assisted by ensuring that as many components were common to the different classes, such as boilers and motion, which kept costs down by large-scale production runs and reducing spares holdings to an acceptable number. Also, some production procedures, such as finishing off parts, could be omitted without compromising their suitability or effectiveness. The following quote illustrates that eminently: 'Overall economy in production cost was paramount with Webb. He was not inclined to sanction the machining or dressing of surfaces needing those processes only for appearance'.

Sometimes this latter trait produced adverse comment on the generally rough finish of some locomotive parts, but the locomotives did their job efficiently enough - the simples anyway - and were relatively cheap to run and were certainly robust enough to stand up to hard use. However, this rough finish was to remain a Crewe feature which lasted for many years, finally being put to rest by Stanier, who found fault with the standard of finish on the prototype 'Princess Royal' Pacific, ordering it to be taken back into the works to be finished off properly before the initial display to the LMS Board. This fact is to be found in the chapter on Stanier in H.A.V. Bulleid's *Master Builders of Steam*.

The initial success of the 'Precursor' and 'Precedent' 2-4-0s led Frank to follow those tender types with that layout when it came to tank engines, in the form of a 2-4-0T, his equivalent to the 'Metropolitan' tank. Fifty were built, the first appearing in 1876 with production completed in 1880. Following these came a slightly larger variant in the form of a 2-4-2T. More versatile with their larger bunker capacity, a total of 180 appeared between 1879 and 1890. In later years 40 of the 2-4-0Ts were to be rebuilt as 2-4-2Ts to join the 180 already in service.

In 1880 two further batches of new designs appeared. Firstly ten 0-4-0Ts for shunting work were turned out and then the first '18 inch' goods 0-6-0, or

2-4-0T No. 2250 with open-backed cab.   *John Alsop Collection*

2-4-0T No. 2240 with enclosed cab at Buxton.   *John Alsop Collection*

2-4-2T No. 1365 with 4 ft 6 in. driving wheels, at Willesden in 1924.   *John Alsop Collection*

2-4-2T No. 2288 with 4 ft 6 in. driving wheels.   *John Alsop Collection*

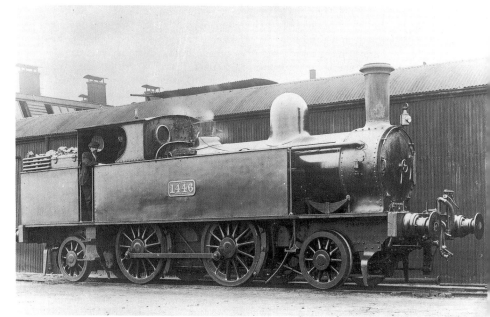

2-4-2T No. 1446. Date unknown but still LNWR days.   *R.S. Carpenter/Lens of Sutton Collection*

'Cauliflower' class 0-6-0 No. 930.   *John Alsop Collection*

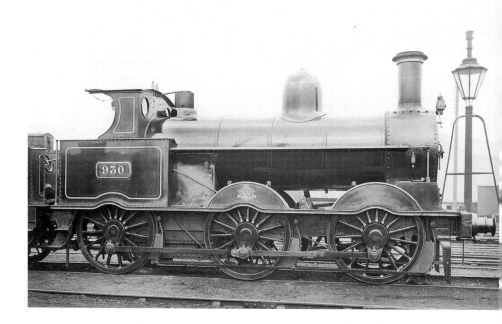

'Cauliflower' emerged. These, at first sight, were an enlargement of the earlier 'Coal Engine' but were, in fact, a new design incorporating the larger cylinders, new boiler and redesigned motion. The nickname came from the placing of the LNWR coat of arms on the middle splasher which, from a distance, was said to resemble the vegetable in question. So useful and sturdy were the 'Cauliflowers' that the class eventually totalled 310 examples, some of which were to survive into British Railways' days. The motion included a new feature, this being the Joy valve gear, which had been patented in 1879. Webb had met Joy at Crewe on 25th May, 1879 and immediately indicated his intention of adopting the Joy gear, as Joy himself wrote in his diary: 'He immediately took to it, as he was designing a new type of big express goods engine, and the gear gave him very large bearings'. Large bearings were essential for a goods locomotive where heavy pulling at low speeds produced high loads on the driving axles. He also arranged with Joy the terms of payment for the rights to use this patent, a protracted process not completed satisfactorily until the autumn of that year. Considering the vast number of future LNWR locomotives to use that gear, this was a particularly astute move. Its simplicity precluded any tinkering by Webb to adjust it such that he could lay claim to an improved version.

David Joy had shown considerable interest in Frank's compound experiments as one of his early patents was for a four-cylinder compound locomotive which employed a divided drive to uncoupled axles, the result being a 4-2-2-0 layout. Whether or not this design had any influence on Webb's forthcoming 3-cylinder compound exercise is not clear, but seems possible, as he was noted for adapting other people's ideas in his own idiom. That early compound design of Joy's was interesting in that the cylinders were all outside, stacked in the Vauclain manner (i.e. one on top of the other) and the two pairs of driving wheels were of different diameters. No interest could be found in this proposal and the patent was never proceeded with. However, once he was aware of Webb's interest in compounds and, bearing in mind the valve gear adoption proposed for the new 0-6-0, Joy schemed a compound version of that locomotive. This was two-cylindered, with 16 inch high pressure and 24 inch low pressure cylinders, with a simpling valve to enable starting with high pressure steam fed to both cylinders. He sent copies of this to Webb, who appeared not to consider this proposal, preferring to launch out into his 3-cylinder approach.

The Institution of Mechanical Engineeers (IMechE) summer meeting of 1880 was held at Barrow-in-Furness in August of that year. By now Frank was on the Council of that Institution and had arranged for Joy to give a paper at that venue - a paper accompanied by an example of his latest locomotive sporting the valve gear, the '18 inch' Goods 0-6-0.

The new design had appeared as this prototype and was joined by nine more in 1882. The balance of the eventual total of 310 built were turned out from 1887. Webb had been installed as Locomotive Superintendent for almost 10 years by 1882 and the slow build-up of the new 0-6-0 was occasioned by rebuilding the 'DX ' class (*see below*) providing adequate motive power for much of the freight needs. There also was considerable investment in other designs, particularly the first compounds, which would have made it difficult to find the required capital

'Cauliflower' class 0-6-0 No. 439 on a passenger train at Colwyn Bay.   *John Alsop Collection*

'Cauliflower' class 0-6-0 No. 147.   *John Alsop Collection*

'Cauliflower' class 0-6-0 No. 1475 with an up goods train at Farington Junction, south of Preston.
John Alsop Collection

'Cauliflower' class No. 84 on an excursion run from Wolverhampton to Derby in 1903; at Walsall just before starting judging by the whistle. Note the almost immaculate condition of the engine.
R.S. Carpenter Collection

'Special DX' No. 1651 in original form without cab.   *LNWR Society Collection*

Rebuilt 'DX' No. 1600 on excursion duties at Walsall *c.*1903.   *R.S. Carpenter Collection*

and workshop capacity to implement the 0-6-0 programme more fully in the early days had it been needed.

The year 1881 also saw the start of a large programme involving the rebuilding of the 'DX' 0-6-0. This type had proved so successful that Webb decided that an upgrade would be economically sound. The programme started cautiously with one example being rebuilt with a 'Coal Engine' boiler set to 140 psi as a prototype. The new locomotive so produced became known as the 'Special DX' and proved to be equally at home on passenger and freight work, a genuine mixed-traffic type, capable of quite high speed work on the former duties. In all 500 of the 'DX' class were eventually rebuilt to this format, a fact which considerably prolonged the life of the original design and rendered the '18 inch' goods unnecessary until the 1890s.

Next on the tank engine front was the 0-6-2T, or 'Coal Tank', which appeared in 1881. Based on the '17 inch' 0-6-0, or 'Coal Engine', this useful design was initially aimed at goods usage, but the brakes were abominable for controlling the British unfitted goods, more so as the brake blocks initially used were wooden and wore quickly. However, the lighter passenger trains of the day demanded less brake power and so the class was eventually found more use on such services as the years went by. These tanks were almost entirely built of standard parts and, as such, were cheap to produce. But there were some features not conducive to good engineering. For example, the connection between the front and rear tanks was via a trunking across the footplate floor, which presented a hazard to the crew. Three hundred were built in total with some 64 lasting into BR days, one of which is happily preserved on the Keighley & Worth Valley Railway, where it has been restored to working order.

Frank's inventive skills allied to his egotistical approach to his work combined to give him a belief that his schemes were always amongst the best, if not *the* best available. He steadfastly refused to contemplate the work of others, apart from the single case of the Joy valve gear. Likewise, for all of his career, he refused to have anything to do with the Association of Railway Locomotive Engineers (ARLE). He did not feel like sharing his design schemes with other Locomotive Superintendents. Group discussions were not his cup of tea. He was fiercely protective of the ideas that flowed from his active mind, so much so, that any flaws in them were quite probably swallowed up by his continual probing for cost control.

With that sort of mentality it becomes reasonable to understand why some basic errors remained as part of the design philosophy. His control over all that went on at Crewe was so complete that no one seemed confident enough to dare to question the rigid demands of their chief. Production methods, cost control and general works efficiency were exemplary under Webb, however, some of his introductions did cause problems. A case in point being the trials with steel fireboxes in which his desire to use as much home-produced steel as possible resulted in the tubes being made from Crewe steel sheet formed by an outside contractor, Jas. Russell & Sons at Wednesbury, who had the specialised equipment necessary. Whilst steel fireboxes were used to a small extent, it would remain until the 20th century for them to become a more standard feature in the UK.

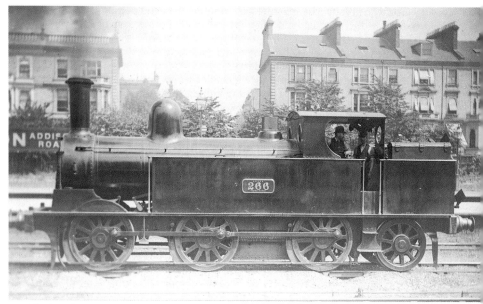

'Coal Tank' 0-6-2T No. 266 at Kensington Addison Road in west London. *John Alsop Collection*

A pair of 'Coal Tanks', Nos. 1251 and 679, await the right away at Swansea Victoria on a local passenger service *c.*1923. *R.S. Carpenter/Lens of Sutton Collection*

The Clarke & Webb chain brake was another case in point. This was a modification of the Clarke chain brake by Webb - here the economical streak comes to the fore in the small but subtle modification of an established invention such that Frank had his name attached to it, in order to ensure that the LNWR did not pay royalties to Clarke.

The brake system consisted of a strong chain carried under the centre of the train which operated the brakes upon being tightened by winding round a fixed shaft driven by a friction wheel system connected to one of the guard's van axles. The driver had a windlass on the left hand side of the cab by which he could wind in a cord to trigger the friction wheel on the front set of fitted carriages. Before the train started the driver had to apply the brake and the guard to observe that the trip mechanism applying the brakes was working, and indicate this to the driver. Thus the driver could apply the brake, but he could not control or adjust the application. For the remainder of the train, the guard operated the brakes by moving a lever causing the friction wheels to come into contact, the resulting tightening of the chain applying the brakes over those coaches not affected by the driver's application. The engines were, in the years of introduction of this system, unbraked, apart from the tender handbrake, so it was a combination of driver and guard who were called upon to provide the braking action for all normal and emergency stops.

Two distinctive features attributed to the reasoning behind the adoption of this crude device were, firstly, it was cheap to install which fitted Moon's desire to minimise on costs and, secondly, train speeds were still sufficiently low and a really powerful brake was not necessary for normal operation. Where it really fell down was on emergency operation, the only means of communication from the driver or passengers being by a most unreliable communication cord which operated a trigger mechanism on each van. The resulting emergency stop could be violent in the extreme sometimes resulting in the train parting. It remained for the Board of Trade to bring in legislation in 1889 enforcing provision of a continuous and automatic braking system on all passenger trains and fast goods before the LNWR reluctantly gave up what could only be described as an inadequate means of braking trains.

However, in 1880, the steam brake appeared on the batch of 'Precedent' 2-4-0s built that year. This gave the drivers the ability to control normal stops without the need to rely on what must sometimes have been erratic braking caused by the guard's applications.

In March 1881, Frank's mother died, just a year short of a Golden Wedding anniversary. The Revd Webb, himself in failing health, resolutely stayed in his living and, once the grieving was over, continued to serve his small flock at Tixall. For some time now, his sister Mary had been living at the Rectory, looking after her ageing parents, for she never married. Frank's elder brother, Arthur, had recently been appointed as the Vicar of St Paul's, Coppenhall, Crewe from his earlier position as Vicar of Dalton, Lancashire. So the two brothers travelled up from Crewe to join the rest of the family at the graveside to bid a fond farewell to a much-loved mother. Having Arthur nearby in Crewe gave Frank the company of a close family member for social occasions and a trusted confidant should he need one.

To divert briefly from locomotive design and production matters, Frank was also turning his mind to the matters of track work on the LNWR. His plans were to introduce steel sleepers to make the entire permanent way of that material. By 1875 the combined iron and steel rail had been discontinued now that the cost of steel had been reduced enough to make an all-steel rail cheaper and it seemed logical to use that material for sleepers as well. He accordingly had the permanent way drawing office prepare designs for track employing the steel sleepers which were then produced in substantial quantities for trials on the main lines from 1880. However, the resulting assembly proved to be rather too noisy when compared to normal wooden sleepers and the experiment slowly faded even though Webb kept bringing out different designs. The inherent flexibility of wooden sleepers led to quieter running and could not be bettered by steel so the scheme was not pursued any further. In typical Webb fashion, examples of the all-steel track work were displayed with the legend 'F.W. Webb system' marked on the sleepers. Only 56 miles of track were laid with the steel sleepers, and of these some 44 had been replaced by wooden ones by the turn of the century.

Frank was beginning to formulate his ideas on compound locomotives and we have seen that he had become involved with the Joy valve gear and David Joy in particular had become a close acquaintance. In 1882 Joy wished to promote his valve gear in the USA and arranged to repeat his IMechE paper, given at the Barrow meeting in 1879, over there. Clearly he had discussed compounds with Frank on many occasions and offered to prepare a paper on them to take over with him. Frank agreed with this immediately, it would provide excellent publicity for his work on the LNWR as well as laying the foundation for a possible introduction of his designs and ideas in the USA. His own foray across the Atlantic had given him a good idea as to the best places in the railway engineering sphere for Joy to visit and he passed on several suggestions regarding this. The compound paper was monitored and, according to Joy's diaries, Frank went so far as to travel up to Liverpool on the 26th May to lunch with David Joy at the Lime Street Hotel and pass over some of the latest trials data of his own types for inclusion. Joy sailed for the USA later that day on his mission and duly presented the valve gear and compound papers at the meeting of the Master Mechanics (the American equivalent of Locomotive Superintendent) held that year at Niagara.

In February 1882, prior to his visit, Joy had corresponded with E.J. Wootten, President of the Philadelphia & Reading Railroad (P&RR) and furnished the P&RR technical department with drawings of his valve gear, which was intended to be fitted experimentally to a large passenger engine on that line. It was hoped that this modification could be prepared to coincide with his paper, as the IMechE paper had involved a live demonstration of the '18 inch' Goods which resulted in the adoption by Webb of Joy gear thereafter. He was hoping for a similar outcome in the USA.

Joy spent much of his time in the USA going around the locomotive works suggested by Webb, both of many railroads and private builders. At some of them he found the standardization so entrenched that a change to his valve gear would involve a radical change to the production and manufacturing procedures. 'Found them all in a groove [he wrote] not much chance for introducing my gear; can't change their routine.' However, he had one success for sure. Having visited the P&RR on the 12th June, to view progress on his gear there, he received a telegram on the 20th at Niagara from their Mr Paxson, the Master Mechanic, to tell him of the satisfactory trials of his valve gear on the modified locomotive. On the 26th June he returned to Philadelphia for a run on this locomotive hauling an 18-car train and collected a considerable amount of test data to bring home with him.

On 27th March, 1883, Frank's father passed away. He was aged 77 and had been Rector of Tixall for 52 of those years. The funeral was on the 31st March, at Tixall, with the service being held in the church that the Revd Webb had faithfully served for so long. Frank and his brothers and sister were there, in the company of a large number of the clergy from the Rural Deanery of Stafford, for from 1858 to 1871 the Revd Webb had been Rural Dean of Stafford. Other representatives were present from the Staffordshire General Infirmary, the Savings Bank, the Coton Hill Asylum, the Talbot & Anson Friendly Society and the Staffordshire Clergy Widows & Orphans Society. All these institutions had benefited from his services over the years. The Trent Valley Horticultural Society, the formation of which resulted from a suggestion by the Revd Webb in 1869, was also represented. Frank and his siblings had always been close to their father, whom they had to thank for their early education. The Revd Webb, senior, was greatly missed.

By now Frank was heavily involved in the design and development of the express compounds. The story of these locomotives is such that it warrants a Chapter of its own to clearly describe their development. But before launching into that, there is one crucial feature to be noted, that of the developments in carriage production at Wolverton. This was under Richard Bore who, although he was the Carriage Superintendent in his own right, worked closely with Webb on matters associated with carriage design. When Webb assumed office it was not long before he and Bore began to discuss how the carriage stock should progress. Bore was strongly in favour of four- and six-wheeled vehicles, these being relatively light and inexpensive to construct. He also was an opponent of the use of bogies. However, this latter trait was not too much of an embarrassment as, up to his retirement in 1886, the bogie vehicle was a relative rarity in Britain. Frank Webb enthusiastically encouraged this thinking, but eventually realised that eight-wheeled stock was inevitable. The outcome was that unique eight-wheeled carriage with the inner axles rigid and the outer ones incorporating his radial truck to enable curves to be safely negotiated. The first examples were of 42 ft length and this type of chassis was applied to passenger carriages, sleeping cars and Post Office vans, of which many examples served for over 40 years. Frank supported his backing of Bore by claiming this type of eight-wheeler reduced the rolling that was often associated with early bogie vehicles.

On Bore's retirement in 1886, he was succeeded by C.A. Park who advocated the introduction of bogie stock, accompanied by a lengthening, first to 45 ft in 1896, then to 50 ft by the following year, for standard vehicles. He had taken note of the growth of passenger traffic demands. This trend, however, contributed towards one major effect - the increase in amenities being provided for the passenger meant that the tare weight, in terms of weight per seat, grew dramatically. Train weights were, in the 1890s, to grow substantially and here we come to a point where locomotive performance, in terms of hauling power, was beginning to be outstripped. Problems lay ahead, particularly with the added urge to increase speeds overall after the 1888 Races to the North.

The increased weight was a key factor in the problems which beset Frank in his development of a family of locomotives to cope with passenger traffic needs. In the near future, by 1897, with the introduction of the Anglo-Scottish express, the average composition of this important train was 10 all-corridor bogie carriages - nearly 300 tons tare - and the locomotives for such services were still relatively small, when compared to those appearing elsewhere in Britain.

May 1888 saw an experiment, started at Frank's suggestion, for hauling canal boats using one of the works' 18 in. gauge locomotives over a length of the Shropshire Union Canal. Track was laid for approximately one mile along the Middlewich branch of this waterway and the locomotive hitched to two narrow-boats. The particular engine used was *Dickie*, one of a pair built to Webb's design by the 'firm' of William Rylance. This was, in fact, an employee of the LNWR at Crewe whose task was to build the 18 inch gauge locomotives. He clearly had quite a sense of humour, for he was reputed to have signed the drawings 'William Rylance & Co.' Frank appeared to gloss over this rather tongue-in-cheek appellation. The experiment seemed promising, with a speed of 7 mph being achieved. Following this, two further boats were attached for another trial. Webb himself attended the trials and a later test showed the small engine to be capable of hauling as many as eight boats. After this, however, no further trials appear to have taken place and the scheme never took off.

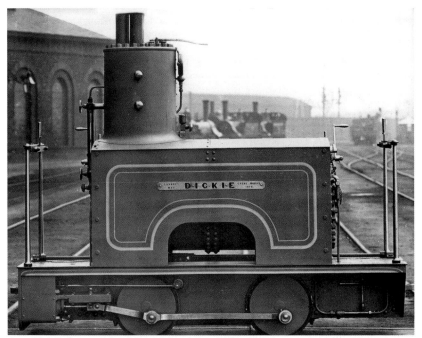

An official photograph of 0-4-0 locomotive *Dickie*. This locomotive entered service on Crewe works' 18 in. gauge system in May 1876. In May 1888 *Dickie* was used for hauling canal barges on a section of the Middlewich branch of the Shropshire Union Canal.

E. Talbot Collection

Chapter Seven

The Three-Cylinder Compounds

Webb was first attracted to the consideration of a compound locomotive by the reports of a successful application of the principle in France in 1876, when a two-cylinder compound 0-4-2T appeared on the Bayonne-Biarritz Railway to the design of Anatole Mallet. A small batch of locomotives to this design were built and proved to be the catalyst for a large number of future developments of two-cylinder compounds throughout the world. The potential of using the expansive properties still inherent in exhaust steam was attractive to many engineers who immediately realised that, properly used, this should enable economies to be made in both water and fuel consumption.

In his continual search for economical operation, Frank saw much to be offered in the employment of compounding in addition to that mentioned above. These were:

(i)   A more even turning moment due to the larger cut-off associated with compound operation.
(ii)   A reduced maintenance cost due to (i).
(iii)   A potentially better acceleration due to (i).
(iv)   Easier firing for a given power output due to the reduction in fuel required.

The matters of reduced specific fuel and water consumption plus the maintenance savings were attractive to reduce the costs of the operating department. They were therefore immediately picked out as features for making the case for funding the development of compound locomotives on the LNWR. Anything which offered cost savings was, following Webb's recommendation of it to Moon, likely to be supported by the required finance.

Webb started cautiously, as any good engineer should, and tried out the concept by following the developments in France. An old 2-2-2 was brought into Crewe works for conversion to a two-cylinder compound. This was simply achieved by lining up one of the two 15 inch outside cylinders to 9 inches. The exhaust from this was fed, via a receiver, across to the other, unmodified, cylinder. In 1878 this straightforward conversion was put to work on light branch duties and its performance, in terms of coal and water consumption, carefully noted for comparison with other unmodified locomotives of the same type.

The experiment was successful, so compounds it was to be - but not a two-cylinder variant. Webb started scheming a three-cylinder compound, initially with one centre high-pressure inside cylinder feeding two outside low-pressure cylinders. We know this, because Webb himself was talking about this being the logical layout in 1879. However, that layout did not appear on the final design, instead there were two outside high-pressure cylinders of 11 inches diameter and a single inside low-pressure cylinder of quite massive size, 26 inches. Quite what brought about this change is a little unclear but the most logical reasons seem to be either the ease of starting with the outside cranks set at 90° to each other or, possibly, the restricted loading gauge of the LNWR placing limits on the diameter of the outside cylinders. A feature of this design, and several others to follow, was that the drive was divided, the low-pressure cylinder connected to the front driving wheels and the high-pressure cylinders connected to the rear driving wheels of the six-wheeled layout that had been based on the 'Precedent' class of 2-4-0. But a peculiarity was present, in that the driving axles were not coupled together, making the final designation a 2-2-2-0. His reason for this can be found in his paper on Compound Locomotive Engines, presented to the ICE in 1883, viz:

> ...and secondly to do away with coupling-rods, while at the same time obtaining a greater weight for adhesion than would be possible on only one pair of driving wheels without rapid destruction of the road. The driving wheels being no longer coupled, there is less grinding action in passing round curves, and it was not even necessary that one pair should be of the same diameter as the other.

Clearly, one reason is that he wished to have the free-running characteristics of the single-driver, for these locomotives were to be employed on the express services. Although this latter argument is a bit tenuous, for Moon, on the grounds of economy of operation, was not pressing for particularly high speeds, even though there was some impending competition for fast Scottish and North of England services beginning to appear from other railways. Another reason for the 2-2-2-0 layout may well have grown from a current worry about connecting rods on high speed engines. There had been a history of some mechanical problems with them. An absolute maximum length of 7 ft 9 in. had been postulated as being the feasible limit which should not bend under inertia stresses at speed. In fact this feature had permeated overseas for, in 1886, Alfred de Glehn at Mulhouse brought out his first four-cylinder compound, a 2-2-2-0. Like Webb's early compounds, the de Glehn design had a long grate which called for a long wheelbase between the driven axles and would have called for a coupling rod greater than the prescribed maximum. There was also the current belief that coupling rods cramped a locomotive's performance.

Probably, the main driver behind Frank's compound designs was that of fuel consumption. Even though coal was economically priced at 7s. 0d. per ton after the 1870s rise and fall, it still represented a substantial part of the running costs in the Locomotive Department. It was the one feature which could be used to lower these costs. The capital cost of the locomotive itself was determined by its size and thereby the cost of turning the raw materials into the finished product. The crews' wages were, to all intents and purposes, a fixed charge. So really the only variable was the fuel cost. Frank himself indicated this in an interview reported in the *Railway Magazine* for 1900: '...combined with my desire to economise the quantity of fuel used that caused me to go so exhaustively into the question of compound engines and adopt that system'. Perfectly sound reasoning in itself, but the final number of locomotives eventually involved, some 360 out of over 3,200 by 1900 (11¼ per cent), could not have had a dramatic effect on the LNWR total fuel costs. A bolder approach, in which a compound system less fraught with difficulties in operation had been adopted, with even larger numbers of engines being built, might have resulted in greater savings overall.

In the above context, it seems a pity that Frank did not stay with his original three-cylinder layout, with the single high-pressure cylinder, for this in later years was very successfully used on the Midland Railway/London, Midland & Scottish Railway (LMS) compounds, of which some 240 were built over the years. He might have had great success and the compound's use in Britain been much greater in extent. However, the restricted loading gauge on the LNWR probably put a limit on the outside cylinders which, being the low-pressure ones, could have encroached on such limits.

However, as usual, no one dared question Frank's decisions and the saga of the compounds began to unfold, with a batch of 30 appearing from 1881. These were suitably dubbed the 'Experiments', this being the name given to the prototype of the class, No. 66. The two high-pressure cylinders did ensure that the locomotive could be started without recourse to the complexities of a simpling valve, but the relatively low tractive effort would have been a distinct disadvantage when allied to the restricted adhesion available from the single axle when starting heavy trains.

The 'Experiments' entered service and proved only reasonably satisfactory and had some inherent disadvantages, mainly due to the large middle cylinder. The piston of this could not be adequately balanced to alleviate the large reciprocating mass and, at speed, the valve provided could not pass the steam in and out adequately, this resulting in considerable back-pressure in the transfer receiver.

Nevertheless, Webb was sufficiently encouraged to go ahead and order the design of a further series of three-cylinder compounds, the 'Dreadnought' class. Again a 2-2-2-0, this class employed cylinders of 14 and 30 inch diameter for high and low pressure circuits respectively. They also had a bigger boiler, but otherwise incorporated no major technical improvement over the 'Experiments'. Forty were authorized and appeared from 1885.

So 70 new locomotives had been built with features adversely affecting their performance, but Webb still persisted in following the compound path - as though he was determined to produce a fleet of outstanding and economical engines to give the LNWR the edge over other railways. We see in the episodes surrounding the express compounds the stubbornness of the man coming through, plus the reluctance of anyone daring to query his reasoning. With his autocratic stance clearly being asserted, there was no room for manoeuvre in the design office to subtly bring about any changes. No advice could be proffered to make him stop and review his philosophy.

The early compounds, whilst initially having enthusiastic support from the technical Press soon, from their early disappointing performance, gathered a stream of adverse comment in the pages of *Engineering*, a widely circulated magazine. This commenced in September 1885 and continued to January 1886 by which time over 32,000 words had accumulated from a correspondent naming himself 'Argus'. Frank made no effort to reply to these damaging articles but made a point when he arranged the names for the 1886 batch of 'Dreadnought' compounds. No. 2056 was rolled out of Crewe bearing the name *Argus*, to be followed shortly by *Autocrat*. Despite the fact that these articles

'Experiment' class 2-2-2-0 3-cylinder compound No. 520 *Express*.   *John Alsop Collection*

'Experiment' class 2-2-2-0 No. 307 *Victor* at Shrewsbury (Crewe Junction).

John Alsop Collection

'Dreadnought' class 2-2-2-0 3-cylinder compound No. 2 *City of Carlisle*.   *John Alsop Collection*

'Dreadnought' class 2-2-2-0 No. 643 *Raven* at Manchester (London Road).

John Alsop Collection

Backhead detail of 'Dreadnought' class 2-2-2-0 No. 2062 *Herald,* partly stripped.

'Dreadnought' No. 1379 *Stork* with plenty of steam, rests by Stafford No. 6 box, *c.*1904.
R.S. Carpenter Collection

'Dreadnought' class 2-2-2-0 No. 2063 *Huskisson* passes Bushey water troughs.
John Alsop Collection

The LNWR Royal Train in 1887 is headed by 'Dreadnought' 3-cylinder compound No. 416 *City of London*.   *Author's Collection*

'Dreadnought' *Marchioness of Stafford* still well maintained in 1904 and with the crew taking a short break at Rugby.   *R.S. Carpenter Collection*

were detrimental to him as a locomotive designer he had sufficient sense of humour to strike back by this adoption of his antagonist's name.

However, some more adverse criticism of the compounds during the discussion of an IMechE paper by George Marié on locomotive fuel consumption in 1884, led to Frank, who had not been present, resigning from the Institution in 1885, clearly dissatisfied by the reporting of the criticism in the published Proceedings.

He was never one to take advice from contemporaries, which explains his continual refusal to get involved in ARLE matters. This was particularly unfortunate, for that august body always acted as a sounding board for the latest design features coming along, which were discussed and, if practicable, adopted to improve locomotive performance on other railways. However, the ARLE was in temporary abeyance during the 1880s and not to resume its meetings until 1889, by which time the compound story on the LNWR was well developed and irreversible.

Despite his ignoring of the ARLE, Frank was always ready to enter into discussion with technical opposite numbers, on his own ground especially. Aspinall frequently dropped in from Inchicore to pick up the latest trends but, try as he may, Frank could not convince him utterly on the merits of compounding.

There was one feature of the Webb three-cylinder concept which made the locomotives identifiable at the outset. This was that the exhaust produced two very loud beats per revolution of the driving wheels. Contemporary reports of hearing the approach of a compound at speed indicated that the observer was considerably startled to find the train passing at a much higher speed than anticipated by the exhaust beats.

In 1883, on one of his regular visits to Crewe, Aspinall raised the possibility of a regular get-together for ex-Crewe men. Frank immediately saw that here could be a good forum for finding out what was happening technically on other railways - at least those employing Crewe-trained persons. He persuaded Aspinall to act as secretary and organiser and, in February 1884, the first of the renowned Crewe dinners took place at the Criterion Restaurant, Piccadilly Circus, Frank himself taking the chair.

However, Frank Webb was sufficiently satisfied with the performance of his latest compounds to have one specially prepared for display at the 1885 Inventions Exhibition. This was held in London at the permanent exhibition centre and educational complex which had been built behind the Royal Albert Hall down Exhibition Road. It has since been replaced by the complex containing the Royal College of Music and the Imperial College of Science & Technology. The LNWR exhibits at this event consisted of a group labelled 'F.W. Webb's Exhibit' and consisted of 'Dreadnought' compound No. 2798 *Marchioness of Stafford* flanked by sundry displays of models of locomotives and components of locomotives, the whole being backed by an impressive display of Webb's patent design of a signal interlocking frame. Frank's ego was certainly at a high for this event!

Perhaps due to the indifferent performance of the first two classes of 2-2-2-0s, when Webb indicated a wish to develop them further only 10 were

This engine took a train from Euston to Carlisle without a stop, a distance of 299 miles, on September 8th, 1895, at an average speed of 51 miles per hour.

L & N.W. 7 CL SIX WHEELED COMPOUND PASSENGER ENGINE BUILT 1890

'Teutonic' compound No. 1306 *Ionic*, built 1890, photographed outside the works on the favourite spot, the old Chester line.   *Author's Collection*

A latter-day duty for 'Teutonic' compound *Coptic*, piloting a Jumbo 2-4-0 at Rugby in 1904.
R.S. Carpenter Collection

authorized, in 1889. Ironically, this version, the 'Teutonic' was to be the best of the three-cylinder express types. But they did have one particular feature which mitigated against them, this being the employment of a slip eccentric for the drive to the low pressure cylinder valve. However, this valve was given longer travel which gave the locomotive a much improved high speed performance.

Regarding the slip eccentric, which actually first appeared on the fourth example *Jeanie Deans*, initially this could prove troublesome, particularly when the engine had to be backed onto a train, which would leave the low-pressure cylinder in reverse gear until sufficient forward movement occurred to reset it to forward gear. There are accounts of vigorous starts being made with the rear wheels slipping and the front wheels spinning backwards to oppose the traction. This was easily remedied by giving the driver the ability to open the low-pressure receiver to atmosphere at the start. Once this modification was in place, the 'Teutonics' gave a good account of themselves on express duties. The slip eccentric was eventually fitted to all the 'Dreadnoughts' and a number of the 'Experiments'.

A good example of the reliability of the 'Teutonic' batch of compounds may be illustrated by the example of No. 1304 *Jeanie Deans*, which from January 1891 to August 1899 hauled the 2.00 pm down from Euston as far as Crewe and returned with the 7.32 pm up. The only times it was not on these services over all those years was when it was in for routine maintenance. On 1st July, 1893 the down train was given new corridor stock then being introduced and became known as the 'Corridor'. Invariably when the compound was in for maintenance, the train was double-headed, which indicates the capability of the 'Teutonic' class when in good hands. Another good performance for a 'Teutonic' on record was a run of 299 miles from Euston to Carlisle with No. 1306 *Ionic* on 8th September, 1895. The train weight was modest, just 151 tons, but the resulting average speed of 51 mph speaks of a sprightly performance.

Other records of the 'Teutonics' showed them to be powerful and capable locomotives. This can be backed up by reference to other creditable runs. Firstly, one splendid run from Preston to Penrith with 10 bogies of 295 tons in which the 72.2 miles were covered in 89 minutes. The minimum speed at Summit for this unbanked effort was just below 30 mph. For a mainly uphill struggle this was a creditable effort and gives a good idea as to the potential of the class. Secondly, was that of No. 1307 *Coptic* on a run from Euston to Crewe in 1895 with a 220 ton load, in which the 158.1 miles were covered in 172 minutes, an average speed of 56.8 mph.

In 1895 an interesting experiment took place. Frank decided to try out a triple-expansion compound variant of the 'Teutonic' series. This he hoped might show some promise, and accordingly No. 1303 *Pacific* was built as a continouous expansion engine. However, this experiment proved somewhat of a disappointment and at its first general overhaul this locomotive was rebuilt to the standard compound condition. Some years later, in 1896 to be precise, Frank had another attempt at a continuous expansion three-cylinder engine by modifying the original compound experimental locomotive, 2-2-2 No. 1874, to a true marine-type triple expansion type. However, it proved a complete failure,

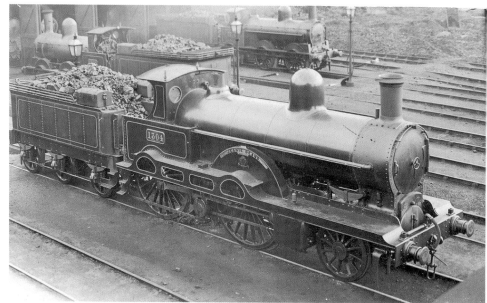

Two views of 3-cylinder 'Teutonic' class 2-2-2-0 No. 1304 *Jeanie Deans* at Shrewsbury.
(Both) John Alsop Collection

being practically incapable of moving itself, let alone a train. No further attempts were made along these lines as Webb had decided to follow the four-cylinder compound for future developments from now on.

In retrospect, a more cautious approach to the compound developments might have resulted in fewer of the earlier, less satisfactory, versions and more of the acceptable 'Teutonics'. It is also puzzling as to why more good points of these were not applied to the 'Experiments' and 'Dreadnoughts' to improve their decidedly poor performance. Maybe this would have been seen by Webb as an admission of his failure to produce a satisfactory design in the early days of compound developments.

With the early compounds being widely publicised, a request to borrow one for trials came from the London & South Western Railway (LSWR). William Adams, that line's Locomotive Superintendent, wished to try out compounding without going to the expense of designing and building such a locomotive. Accordingly, No. 300, of the first 'Experiment' class, was dispatched to the LSWR and put into service on the Waterloo to Exeter expresses. This run was 171 miles with six stops and 4 hours 13 minutes allowed. A light load out of Waterloo, about 150 tons, reduced to 110 tons at Salisbury, was the norm.

No. 300 struggled with this schedule, much time being lost in the laborious starts. Some hard driving kept the schedule more or less to time but at the expense of high coal consumption. The LSWR's higher speeds, compared to the LNWR requirements, served to eliminate the fuel saving advantage of the compound. The locomotive eventually returned to Crewe with suitable thanks, and Adams proceeded to try out the Worsdell-von-Borries two-cylinder compound system by rebuilding one of his 7 ft 4-4-0s, but never pursued compounding any further following trials with this.

The Webb compounds clearly attracted a lot of interest from other countries, for some examples were to be built privately for export. The first, in 1884, was 2-2-2-0 of the 'Dreadnought' class built by Sharp, Stewart for the Western Railway of France. Another, of the same class, was ordered by the Pennsylvania Railroad from Beyer, Peacock in 1888. Whilst the French railways were to be much involved in compound locomotives from this time, the vast majority were four-cylindered, their three-cylindered types being of the single high pressure and two low pressure layout, plus a sprinkling of two-cylindered variants. The Pennsylvania RR, apart from this one example of Webb's expertise, and a foray into compound Mallets in 1919, was never to adopt the compound philosophy extensively for its designs. Other examples were for Argentina (one in 1884 from Dübs), Brazil (one in 1885 from Sharp, Stewart); Austria (one in 1884 from Sharp, Stewart); two in 1884 for the Antofagasta Railway in Chile by Robert Stephenson & Co., this being a narrow gauge (2 ft 6 in.) 4-2-4-2 tank version. The only sizeable order came from India in 1884, this being a batch of 10 for the Oudh and Rohilkund Railway supplied through Dübs & Co.

A notable feature of the nameplates for all of the Webb compounds was the addition of the inscription 'F.W. WEBB'S SYSTEM' in small letters under the name itself, the nameplate having been deepened to accommodate this. Even the exported examples sported 'WEBB'S PATENT NO 2' for the French, and 'F.W. WEBB'S SYSTEM' for the American, engines.

Sent to the Chicago Exhibition in 1893 where it gained the gold medal for excellence of workmanship and subsequently ran a L. & N.W. train from Chicago to New York, the only British train ever run in America. Specially painted white and with the Royal Arms in honor of Queen Victoria's Diamond Jubilee in 1897. Has run 473,759 miles to end of Sept. 1904.

COMPOUND PASSENGER ENGINE "QUEEN EMPRESS"

'Greater Britain' class 2-2-2-2 compound No. 2054 *Queen Empress* represented the LNWR at the 1893 Chicago Exhibition, gaining a gold medal. Here seen in the special white livery in honour of Queen Victoria's Diamond Jubilee in 1897.   *Author's Collection*

'Greater Britain' class No. 2051 *George Findlay* at Carlisle.   *John Alsop Collection*

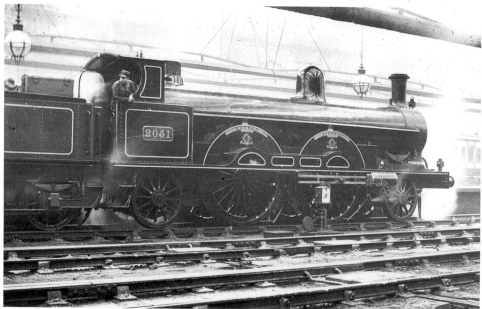

In 1891, Sir Richard Moon, who had received a Baronetcy in 1887, retired from his position as Chairman of the LNWR Board. Lady Moon had died earlier that year and his loss had brought about the wish to retire. Frank had lost a capable and reliable supporter but, on the other hand, the departure of Moon had removed a long-standing opposition to larger locomotives. Moon's type of management ideals had fitted perfectly with Frank's design aspirations, with the latter accepting the constraints incurred by the Chairman's obsession with cost minimisation and thereby small engines. LNWR locomotives up to now were small and, placed beside equivalent designs of other railways, this was all too evident. Yet they did good work. In terms of hauling power per unit weight they were amongst the best. This is perhaps amplified by a quotation from Webb himself: 'I am not so much concerned in excessively high rates of speed as in getting a very heavy train along the line at a reasonable speed' (*Railway Magazine*, Feb. 1900).

Webb responded to the cessation of continued pressure for small economic locomotives with further compound developments in the form of two new types, firstly a stretch of the 'Teutonic' to a 2-2-2-2, the 'Greater Britain' class. Unfortunately, all the good points of the 'Teutonics' disappeared and this class appeared with a new, longer, boiler incorporating a 'combustion chamber' half-way along its length. This was certainly the wrong place to put it and made the boiler very difficult to manufacture and maintain. There were still no coupling rods, and with uneven track sometime placing a disproportionate amount of weight on the rear carrying wheels, starting could be a problem with the reduced adhesion on the rear driving wheels. The slip eccentrics were also retained.

Never popular, the 10 examples produced over the 1891-94 period were followed by 10 more between 1894 and 1898, the latter identical but for the driving wheels of 6 ft 3 in. diameter, as against the 7 ft 1 in. of the earlier variant. These, known as the 'John Hick' class, were even more mediocre in performance. However, the 'Greater Britain' class was deemed sufficiently advanced and up-to-date enough to be sent to the Chicago Exhibition of May 1893 to represent the British locomotive scene. The second of the class, named *Queen Empress*, was duly prepared at Crewe in a special white overall livery, with light blue edging and smoke box and dispatched on its trans-Atlantic voyage. The return to Crewe was in January 1894, complete with the gold medal awarded, and it was put into traffic later that month.

It was in 1892 that the final elimination of the non-automatic vacuum braking systems was achieved on the LNWR. As recently as 1890 there had been over 600 vehicles still fitted with the Clarke-Webb chain brake and over 550 with the simple vacuum brake. These latter two systems had, at last, expired being replaced by an automatic brake, in this case the vacuum type, in accordance with the Board of Trade requirements.

In 1895 the first of the initial batch, *Greater Britain* itself, was employed on the final stage of the journey of a special train taking delegates to the fifth International Railway Congress back to London after a 3-day tour of railway works. They had visited Swindon Great Western Railway (GWR), Horwich (L&YR), Crewe (LNWR), Darlington (North Eastern Railway), Derby (MR) and

'Greater Britain' class No. 527 *Henry Bessemer* on shed at Shrewsbury.   *John Alsop Collection*

'Greater Britain' class No. 2053 *Greater Britain* at Blisworth.   *John Alsop Collection*

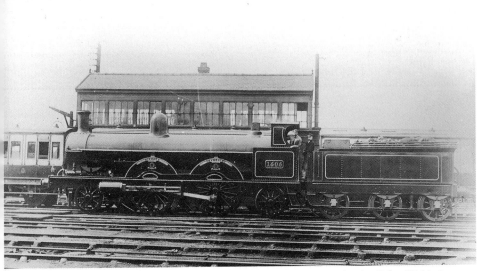

One of the smaller-wheeled second batch of the 2-2-2-2 compounds, the 'John Hick' class
No. 1505 *Richard Arkwright*.   *John Alsop Collection*

'John Hick' class No. 1505 *Richard Arkwright* on Shrewsbury shed.   *John Alsop Collection*

'John Hick' class No. 1536 *Hugh Myddleton* on a passenger train at Colwyn Bay.
John Alsop Collection

'John Hick' class, No. 1548 *John Penn* at Stafford, 1904.   *R.S. Carpenter Collection*

Stratford (Great Eastern Railway). Frank attended this Congress, held at the Imperial Institute, as one of the representatives of the LNWR.

If Webb had had a very determined and capable assistant, perhaps his stubborn determination could have been subtly softened, such that the worst features of some of the compounds could have been eliminated. For, despite their technical shortcomings they were capable, in good hands, of doing good work. Coupling rods would have overcome many starting problems. Theoretically, the compound principle was fuel economic and the smaller values of piston thrusts due to the moderately sized high-pressure cylinders certainly assisted in reducing wear, as witnessed by the large mileages between overhauls eventually achieved. The 'Teutonics' were regularly returning 80,000 miles for that measure, as against 60,000 miles for a typical 'Precedent' 2-4-0.

On the ancillary side of locomotive design, although some 2,000 gallon tenders had been built by Ramsbottom for the 'Problems' working the Irish Mail, Webb tenders were, initially, on the small side. Starting at 1,500 gallons, they were increased to 1,800 gallons, then 2,000 gallons, finishing up at 2,500 gallons in 1902 just before he retired. Small tenders could be tolerated due to the plentiful supply of water troughs on the LNWR main lines. There was also a second reason, the fact that the tender frames were constructed of wood and once tender capacities got to 2,500 gallons any further increase would result in steel frames being required to cope with the weight. Many of the old wood-framed tenders lasted well into the days of Grouping. Coal rails appeared in 1895, at first on passenger engines only.

Once freed from the strict restraints imposed by Moon, Frank immediately began development of larger locomotives for freight services, fully realising the need for them as train weights continued to grow. Industry demanded even greater deliveries of fuel and raw materials to satisfy the call for increased output to meet export and home markets demands. The LNWR had vast quantities of coal to transport around, so freight locomotives were of significant importance.

In October 1892 the first eight-coupled locomotive appeared. It was a two-cylinder simple 0-8-0 employing a boiler based on that of the 'Greater Britain' compound, complete with the combustion chamber half-way along the barrel. The valves, cylinders and motion were based on that of the '18 inch Goods', the cylinders being enlarged to 19 inch diameter. This design signalled the end of 0-6-0 developments for purely freight use and, in fact, no new 0-6-0s were designed for the rest of the days of the LNWR.

Only one example, No. 2524, was built to the above specification, for a year later a further 0-8-0 appeared, delayed by the effects of a prolonged miners' strike on production. This affected the country as a whole and the railways in particular. Crewe works was considerably badly hit, as the steel production dropped to 25 per cent of normal for the last half of 1893. The shortage caused the working week to be reduced to four days and several hundred workmen to be laid off. Eight of the 10 'Greater Britain' express compounds were delayed in completion by this reduction in hours and the next 0-8-0 by almost a year. To cap it all, the LNWR dividend for that year was reduced to 5⅞ per cent from its former 7 per cent.

'A' class 3-cylinder compound 0-8-0 No. 1831.   *John Alsop Collection*

'A' class 0-8-0 No. 2555 on a coal train in the Walsall area *c.*1902-03.   *R.S. Carpenter Collection*

The next example followed the three-cylinder compound concept. The boiler, however, was different in that no combustion chamber was employed, being replaced by recessing the front tube-plate into the boiler by an equivalent distance. The outside high-pressure cylinders used Stephenson valve gear and the single low-pressure cylinder had a slip eccentric, the first time Frank had departed from his favourite Joy gear for many years.

These two 0-8-0s were used for comparative trials which resulted in the compound version being selected for production as the standard heavy goods engine. In all 110 were built between 1894 and 1900, eventually becoming known as the 'A' class. One significant modification retrospectively applied to these first 0-8-0s, and subsequently to be a standard feature of all eight-coupled locomotives on the LNWR, was that the third pair of coupled wheels were made flangeless to facilitate easier operation over sharp curves.

The drive was concentrated onto the second axle and was, at the low speeds involved, particularly smooth. The low speed also eliminated any problems due to the balancing of the large low pressure piston.

Out of all Webb's three-cylinder compounds these 0-8-0s were the most successful for, after comprehensive trials, they showed a saving in coal and water consumptions over those for the simple version of 23 and 24 per cent respectively. They were eventually to live on in rebuilt guise, as simples, into the Grouping era with some entering BR stock.

To contrast with these large locomotives, at the other end of the scale there were a batch of the standard 0-4-0ST shunters on order in 1892 and Webb arranged that three of them were built as 0-4-2ST crane tanks. The original crane fitted had a short jib cleared to lift 4 tons. Two were later fitted with longer jibs capable of lifting 3 tons to increase their working area.

Having had moderate success with his tender compound designs Frank turned his mind to the design of a tank engine variant. In his usual experimental way he ordered the conversion of one of the 'Metropolitan' 4-4-0 tanks to a 4-2-2-0T compound using a similar layout to that of the 'Experiment' 2-2-2-0. The conversion was turned out in February 1884 and entered service, proving the concept worthy of more applications, of which three single versions were built.

These appeared, firstly in the form of a 2-2-2-2T, No. 687 comparable to the 4 ft 6 in. 2-4-2T, being turned out in September 1885, secondly a similar design, No. 600, but with 5 ft 6 in. driving wheels in July 1887 and, thirdly, a 2-2-4-0T layout, No. 777, this latter having 5 ft 2 in. driving wheels. This particular layout was occasioned by the need to provide extra adhesion for starting goods trains. This variant was actually turned out in March 1887 but as it was exhibited at the Manchester Jubilee Exhibition did not enter service until November of that year. It was then found, after a short spell of goods work, on passenger trains between Buxton and Manchester.

Apart from the original 'Metropolitan' conversion, all these compound tanks had the outside valve gear located above the slide bars compared to that below the slide bars as on the 2-2-2-0s. None of these designs was perpetuated and the prototypes eked out their relatively short lives on minor services. They had one distinctive characteristic when applied to passenger services in that they soon acquired a reputation for strong fore and aft surging when pulling hard at slow

'A' class 0-8-0 No. 1801 on a goods train at Carlisle Upperby.   *John Alsop Collection*

'A' class 0-8-0 No. 50 at Shrewsbury.   *John Alsop Collection*

0-4-0ST No. 2526.   *John Alsop Collection*

0-4-0ST No. 3009 at Crewe works.   *John Alsop Collection*

0-4-2ST crane engine No. 3248 built under Webb. Crewe works, 27th August, 1933.
MRT/R.G. Jarvis Collection

0-4-2ST crane engines Nos. 3248 and 3249 at Crewe works.   *John Alsop Collection*

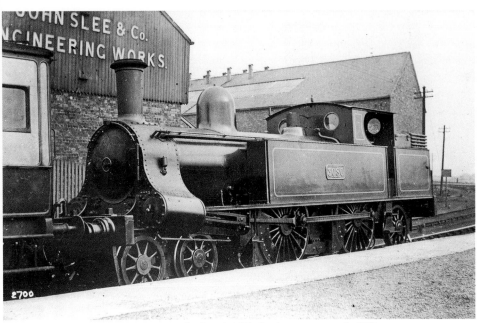

'Metropolitan' 4-4-0T No. 3080 as rebuilt to 4-4-2T wheel arrangement in 1892.
John Alsop Collection

4-2-2-0T 3-cylinder compound No. 3026 was rebuilt from a 'Metropolitan' tank in 1884; until March 1889 it carried the number 2063. *John Alsop Collection*

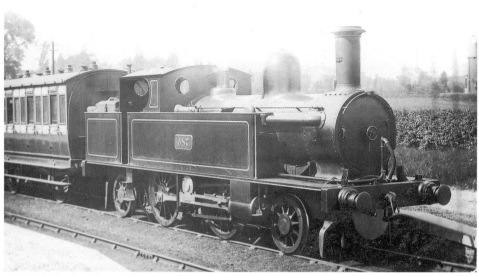

2-2-2-2T No. 687 at Heaton Chapel.   *John Alsop Collection*

2-2-2-2T No. 600 at Buxton.   *John Alsop Collection*

2-2-4-0T No. 777 at Manchester (London Road). *John Alsop Collection*

speeds. This also had been a feature of the 'Dreadnoughts', but in that case the surging was partially dampened by the tender. Tank engines, being coupled directly to the carriages, produced a more marked surging motion and a report written some years later states: 'When leaving Victoria (Underground) a full carriage of passengers were surging backwards and forwards after the manner of a University "eight"'. This refers to No. 687, the second compound tank, which was sent to London and worked on the Mansion House trains for a short while in the same link as the simple engines.

However, let it be said here, that once the crews had got used to the idiosyncrasies of the three-cylinder compounds, the tender versions of these locomotives provided a large amount of revenue service for the LNWR. They ran long mileages between overhauls and were frequently found on 300 ton trains, keeping to the schedule and proving their worth. Webb strongly rebuked any criticism of them, frequently gathering data on their behaviour in service to counteract any attempt to run them down. The worst of the bunch were the 'Experiments', which were quickly relegated to secondary services, usually handled with less experienced crews, and quickly gained a reputation for sluggish starting on stopping services. The 'Dreadnoughts' and 'Teutonics', handled by good drivers, did a great deal of good work with heavy loads, the latter often being timed at speeds up to 90 mph.

So far as three-cylinder compounds were concerned the story ends here, but further compounds were to come in four-cylinder guise coupled with much less unorthodox features. However, before that there are some further local events and more simple locomotive designs to be considered.

Frank Webb.   *Author's Collection*

Chapter Eight

Local Politics, Management and Other Issues

Crewe was granted borough status in 1877. The LNWR was by far the largest employer in the town and very shortly it was obvious that a majority of the Borough Council was of those elected in the railway's interest. In fact, the foremen at the works put considerable pressure on the workers to vote for those candidates. A political battle was inevitably to break out, with the opposing parties, the Liberals in particular, complaining vociferously about the bias towards the railway's interests. Over half the town was built and owned by the LNWR, which was also the largest ratepayer, but the Liberals were keen on wresting power from the strong railway representation. They championed the cause that the railway's influence should be curtailed whilst the public amenities it provided, largely free of charge, were expected to be continued and, in some cases, increased. It seemed strange that this view emanated from a call for 'political freedom' as it was put.

The first person to be elected as Mayor was Dr James Atkinson, a well-known local figure and prominent Conservative politician, who from 1866 had been the LNWR surgeon and had, as such, become a close friend of Webb. He had considerable dealings with the works through the treatment of industrial injuries in the sometimes not very safety-conscious Victorian factory environment. It was his friendship with Webb that led to the two of them being instrumental in the setting up of the railway hospital, one of Webb's many civic benefits to the local community. The finance for this enterprise came from a chance meeting of Webb with a Henry Yates Thompson, son of an old Director of the LNWR, who wished to give the sum of £1,000 for a suitable purpose in memory of his father's connection with the company. Frank immediately thought of the hospital, so long the wish of Dr Atkinson. Representation of this idea at Board level soon provided the land needed from the railway and the Memorial (to Mr Yates) Cottage Hospital was erected, with Frank himself adding to the funds.

One only has to look at the local press archives for Crewe to find how much Frank Webb was drawn into many affairs associated with Crewe. From the earliest days of his Locomotive Superintendency his speeches at many local events are to be found reported in the *Crewe Chronicle* and *Crewe Guardian*. The number and varying kinds of organizations demanding his time and presence point to a very full and busy life outside the confines of Crewe works. Yet he still found time to indulge in some hobbies, notably gardening, which drew him even more into the town's affairs. Whilst some of the outside local interests were inevitably connected to the LNWR he must have felt duty bound to represent the railway's interests at their functions. It was inevitable that he would be drawn into the political arena.

The infamous 'Intimidation' affair associated with the local political scene coincided with Frank's essay into local government. He had already been elected to the town council as an Independent and it was an argument brought about by the minority Liberals that sullied the air in a most unfortunate manner. It emanated from some claims that the LNWR had pressured some of the workers to remove their support from the Liberal candidates at the local elections. It was a complex situation, for the railway had a large interest in the local community, it having been responsible for the growth of Crewe and many of the services available to the inhabitants (water, gas etc.) had been provided with railway money. Churches, hospitals and other amenities had also been provided through the railway. So it was natural that several councillors, Frank amongst them, were from the railway staff. All were in office as Independents, it being politically unwise to ally themselves to either the Liberal or Tory causes. At the start of the affair, the Tories were in the majority on the Council.

In those days the Liberals were more closely allied to the working classes and, as such, their interests were followed closely by the shop floor workers. However, as many of the foremen were of middle class extraction, many with a Public School background, their political leanings would have been towards the Tories. Hence some acrimonious comments to those beneath them would have sparked off some arguments. These arguments led to the dismissal of some workers it seems. Unfortunately, amongst those dismissed were the Chairman of the Crewe Liberal Association, Joseph Jones, and the Secretary of the Crewe Liberal Club, William Urquhart. These were long-serving members of the workforce, with 23 and 33 years in the works respectively. The latter had also acquired a reputation for trouble-making in the past. There was also the major charge of quite severe intimidation in 1885 when, after 150 men had been discharged from the works, it was mentioned that many of these were Liberals and only one a Tory. This added fuel to the flames of political conflict.

This business simmered on through the 1880s, only quieting down during the mid-years approaching the Jubilee of Queen Victoria. In 1886 Frank, reluctantly by all accounts, accepted the position of Mayor of Crewe and was elected as such for the two years from 11th November, 1886. He was not a politically minded person and never fully entered into the fray of local government. After all, he was an Independent and took that mantle seriously. His attitude to the unsavoury events taking place was printed in the *Crewe Guardian* on 26th February, 1887, and is included here: 'You know very well that I sit here as an independent Mayor, and will not allow, if I can help it, any politics to interfere with me, and have never interfered in the politics of this town'. One aspect of politics clearly against his thinking was the dishonesty he found in individuals. His thoughts on policy matters were 'Is it good for the town?' thus putting the inhabitants first in his decisions.

Thankfully his two years as Mayor were relatively trouble-free and his generosity towards the town remained unfettered. By 1890 the Intimidation Affair had petered out and in 1891 Crewe Council consisted of 20 Liberals and four Tories. *Plus ça change!*

Frank relinquished his mayoral duties in 1888 and withdrew from further involvement in local government, not wishing to be further drawn into the political arguments by then at their climax. However, he did remain a County Magistrate and an Alderman of the Cheshire County Council. One highlight of his two-year term as Mayor was the 4th July, 1887, the celebration of Queen

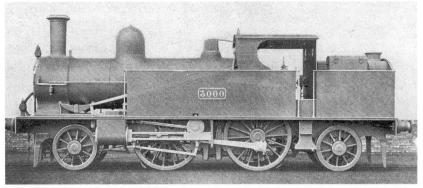

3-cylinder compound 2-2-2-2T as exhibited with the special 3000 number at the Manchester Exhibition of 1887. *Author's Collection*

Victoria's Golden Jubilee. As this date coincided with the 50th anniversary of the opening of the Grand Junction Railway through Crewe the LNWR had given to the town an area of land for its use as a park and made available funds for its preparation for such use. Webb had used his influence with Moon to acquire the land and to provide £10,000 from the LNWR coffers towards the cost of preparing it. In way of thanks for his acquiescence it was arranged for the honorary freedom of the Borough to be conferred on Sir Richard Moon, Bart, as he then was, in acknowledgement of this generous gift by the company. This was duly given to him at the celebrations, to make him the first Honorary Freeman of the Borough. It was also arranged that the 3,000th locomotive to emerge from Crewe works was rolled out with due ceremony on this day. As a matter of interest, the 3,000th locomotive was one of the pair of 3-cylinder compound 2-2-2-2Ts built in 1887 and was given a special number-plate bearing the number 3000 for all the official photographs. It entered service shortly after with the running number 600. The park itself, known appropriately as 'Queen's Park', was officially opened a year later on 9th July, 1888.

The Park layout had been designed jointly by Frank Webb and Edward Kemp and that layout is retained to this day. It is still regarded as one of England's finest parks, with successive curators adding to its facilities through the years. A little instance of Frank's sense of humour is to be found on the gate lodges to this park. One has the outline of a crescent moon on its wall and the other a spider's web. Just a gentle reminder that Moon and Webb were the instigators of this recreational establishment for the citizens of Crewe.

Frank's interests in the local community continued throughout all this time and were many and various. For example the Presidencies included those of the Crewe Philharmonic Society, the Crewe Mechanical Institute Chess and Draughts Club, the Crewe Britannia Bowling Club and the Crewe Shorthand Writers Association.

One of the features of Webb's influence over the departments answerable to his control was the way in which he kept the facts and figures close at hand for those matters concerning the capital involvements of the business. These covered investment costs, returns on those investments, the buying in of raw materials and stocks available of raw materials and spares. With these he was able to evaluate the works' efficiency and the amount of the Locomotive Department's part in the prosperity of the LNWR as a whole.

Discipline was another important part of his management style. He clearly realised that permitting foremen and workers too much freedom in their tasks could bring about a chaotic situation resulting in the loss of efficiency plus slack moments on the shop floor. Tasks were to be organised such that minimal waiting time resulted, and anyone found where they were not normally gainfully employed without just cause would be immediately reprimanded. This is one of the reasons that the works 18 inch gauge tramway system was so important to ensure that components reached the position in the erection shops as and when needed - a first Victorian attempt at the 'just in time' production cycle so prevalent today.

To assist with the above, Webb took advantage of some technological developments that he saw could offer assistance, particularly if they resulted in other cost savings in addition to enhanced efficiency. In the early 1880s he had a basic telephone system installed in the works which enabled him to get in touch with clerks and key officers without the need to employ someone to summon them. He was so pleased with this that the system was expanded to cover the whole of the office block by the mid-1880s.

Parallel with the introduction of telephones, electricity made its first appearance at Crewe in 1878 in the guise of an experimental system for lighting Crewe station. Frank immediately saw the potential of this new means of lighting and powering operations in the works. He saw to it that, for the early days at least, the application of this came under the Locomotive Department. By the late 1880s a small electrical department had been established to deal with the lighting of the works and at other important stations. This was then charged with developing electric drives for some of the shops. Electric arc welding was introduced on a small scale in the early 1890s with additional developments for drilling and reaming. By 1897 some of the line shafting and cranes were employing electric drives. In 1900, such was the demand that a new steam-electric power house appeared to supply much of the works' requirements.

With the introduction of electric lighting at some stations, Frank experimented with its application to trains. 'Problem' class No. 44 *Harlequin* was fitted with a generator mounted on the tender, driven by a Brotherhood three-cylinder engine, the current being supplied to both engine and train. Despite two further iterations on the power source for the generator, this experiment was not perpetuated, being a relatively expensive way of meeting the requirement, but was a very early application of this medium for train lighting.

By the 1890s, the use of electricity was clearly becoming more widespread and was here to stay, a fact which prompted Frank to consider that the main line would, in the future, be electrified and trains would be capable of travelling at very high speeds indeed. At that time, this would have been seen as wishful thinking, but he was a visionary who had a clear view of the potential to be offered as technology advanced towards the 20th century.

Frank Webb was just one of a clutch of outstanding railway engineers to grow from the Victorian age, when that mode of transport was at the forefront of engineering technology. These engineers brought about great advances in the design, production and operation of steam locomotives throughout those years. This ensured the continuation of their usage through into the 20th century until the development of other forms of transportation emerged and the arrival of electric and diesel units eventually displaced them. His autocratic manner tended to hide a perceptive mind continually searching for better ways in which to further the aims of the LNWR. Like Churchward and Fowler to come elsewhere after Webb approached his apogee, he was an early motorist who eagerly took to this new mode of transport for his personal use in leisure moments.

It had been some time since his parents had died and in 1890 Frank was saddened to learn of the death of his brother William, who for the previous 10 years had been Vicar of Alrewas, Staffordshire. He was just 46 and, like Arthur, had been following in his father's footsteps in the Church.

Co-incidental with this sad loss, the fate of the much maligned 'Metropolitan' 4-4-0 tanks, by now long displaced from their early North London services, had to be decided. Six had been withdrawn, of which one example was rebuilt as a three-cylinder compound in February 1884, following the lines of the 'Experiment' class 2-2-2-0s. The other five were scrapped by 1892-93. The remaining 10 were extensively rebuilt as non-condensing 4-4-2 tanks, when they were given new steel boilers, cylinders, bogies, large bunkers and cabs. The result was quite a handsome engine. They were then sent to the Manchester area to be employed on suburban trains and secondary goods services, being withdrawn and scrapped between 1907-11.

As time went on and he further increased his influence over the many differing tasks allied to the LNWR Locomotive Department, adding to them as appropriate, he did not take kindly to criticism of his design aims. He was, undoubtedly, an extremely capable engineer where conventional steam locomotives were concerned, but somewhat rigid in his approach to new ideas once accepted. His handling of the compound story was a case in point, for it took some years of complaints from the Running Departments to hammer home the shortcomings of his three-cylinder types. Had he agreed to the coupling of the driving wheels there might have been considerably less trouble in starting and a smoother application of torque. But Webb was notoriously difficult to dislodge from his perch, particularly when it involved engineering matters. He was, after all, in many ways an outstanding engineer, and he knew it. He had, by this time, got involved in the ARLE to the extent of delegating C.A. Park, the LNWR Carriage and Wagon Superintendent, to join the association so that he had a personal representative to report back on what was being discussed. He had no intention of being left behind in the development race.

One particular area in which Frank took little or no interest was that concerning the power exerted in the works by the foremen. They could, and frequently did, engage and sack workers without any recourse to higher authority. The insecurity of employment thus engendered encouraged the rise of trade unionism at Crewe, which accelerated from the late 1880s. However, a disciplined environment was essential to ensure that the production from a large works was in phase with the constituent parts coming together, over distances of up to a mile, in the erecting shops at the required time. Each shop manager and his team of foremen needed to be aware of the needs further down the production cycle and organize their output to match these. The result of this rigid approach often led to layoffs during slack periods, unless short-time working sufficed. Quite often layoffs or dismissals were coloured by the individual worker's political, or even religious, leanings. The Victorian industrial environment was a tough and biased one indeed.

Whilst he was Works Manager, Worsdell fully supported Webb in maintaining the rigid disciplined approach via his lower echelons of staff. Both he and Webb would note anything likely to result in loss of productivity, with a telling memo immediately dispatched to the relevant foreman.

One feature of the strict accounting system demanded by Moon was the requirement of monthly stores and departmental accounts from Crewe works. As the works were expanded these accounts grew more complicated, particularly when it is realised that between 1870 and 1900 the workforce of the Locomotive Department (which covered engine crews and shed staff) rose from 10,600 to 21,700. A huge force of up to 300 clerks was necessary to deal with all the mass of associated paperwork. To complement this, and produce for himself a guide as to how expenditure was going, Frank introduced a system of graphical statistics to indicate how the changes in the cost of coal and raw materials influenced his department's costs. One figure, often quoted by himself, was that on average the Locomotive Department expenditure absorbed some 11 per cent of the LNWR revenue.

There was, however, one factor in which he excelled, this being the preservation of historic machinery. Whereas other CMEs were to, admittedly in good faith, to order the scrapping of stored obsolete engineering artefacts, Webb, after locating a Trevithick stationary engine of 1814, had it restored to as near to its original condition as possible before ordering it to be stored in the Crewe paint shop. It was, after many years there, donated to the Science Museum, but this was not until LMS days.

In the future it was Churchward and Stanier who were to order the cutting-up of stored historic locomotives on the grounds that they took up valuable space in their respective works at Swindon and Derby.

In concert with similar happenings on the other British railways, 1887 saw the 2nd Cheshire Royal Engineer (Railway) Volunteer Corps founded, following considerable encouragement from Webb. He had sounded out various LNWR officials on the possibility of this after noting the steady growth in the Engineer and Railway Volunteer Corps, which had come from a proposal in 1864 of Charles Manby, the Secretary of the Institution of Civil Engineers. Its purpose was to direct the application of railway transport and labour to the work of National Defence and prepare, in a time of peace, a system on which such duties should be conducted.

The Volunteers soon had 760 men from all departments of the works signed up and formed into six companies. Their first major inspection parade was in July 1888, when the Duke of Cambridge, C-in-C of the British Army, presided at the opening of the Queen's Park. In all 245 of the men were classed as regular reserves liable for call-up in times of emergency. This happened during the Boer War at the end of the century and a company, under the command of a Major Schofield, was dispatched to South Africa on active service.

In typical Webb fashion, he saw to it that this Crewe company had a suitable chaplain, and persuaded his brother Arthur to fulfil this role. He was conveniently close in Crewe and clearly willing to take on this little responsibility for his brother. However, his own choice of church was not that of his brother, but Christ Church which had been built and endowed by the LNWR. He was a regular attendee when in Crewe on Sundays, always depositing a sovereign in the collection plate. If, for any reason he could not be present on any Sunday, he sent the sovereign during the following week.

Frank had, by 1890, acquired a country home, Stanway Manor, near Church Stretton, which must have been a welcome relief to retire to after a busy week at Crewe, as the relentless pressure of his multiplicity of responsibilities surrounded him. The house had been built in 1863 by a William Hotton as 'a gentleman's residence'. The Manor came with 550 acres of land and set him back £12,000. He could be found at this haven on many week-ends, relaxing and indulging in the pursuits appropriate to the country living of his boyhood days, for there was a farm included in this extensive property and Frank was able to play the Country Squire. He clearly took an active part in the farming side of things, for he had installed a narrow gauge railway system to assist in the heavier tasks of moving loads around (manure from mucking out cows, animal feed, bales of straw, etc.). He also could be found pursuing his gardening interests and entertaining some of his circle of friends, amongst whom was a G.R. Jebb. Jebb was a civil engineer by profession, who was employed by Birmingham Council, and the two of them spent many week-ends at Stanway relaxing in the country atmosphere and sharing experiences from their respective careers. He clearly became a close confidant and was to receive a generous legacy in Webb's Will to thank him for that time of companionship.

There is a delightful story concerning Frank Webb and a quick-witted porter. He travelled to and from Stanway Manor by train and, on the return journey was looked after by an elderly porter at Shrewsbury, where he changed trains. His train from Church Stretton was always met by this porter, who carried his bag and rug to the Crewe train and saw him comfortably settled in a first-class compartment. For this the porter received a tip of two shillings. One winter's morning, after handing his helper a generous half-a-crown (2s. 6d.), Frank looked seriously at him and said: 'I suppose you know the company's regulations forbid you to accept gratuities from passengers?' 'Yes, Sir', replied the porter. 'Oh, you do know the rule then?' 'Yes, Sir. Most certainly I'm acquainted with what the Rule Book says about receiving tips from ordinary passengers, but I didn't think it applies to fellow railway servants!' Frank appeared completely deflated at this reply and was too astonished to answer as the porter shut the carriage door. That story became almost a legend on the railway, whilst the old porter continued to meet the Stretton train and see to Frank on Monday mornings.

To return to the gardening interests, for many years Frank was Vice-President of the Crewe & District Chrysanthemum Society and the Crewe Horticultural Society. He frequently entered exhibits (under the name J. Smith) which won prizes at the Crewe Flower Show. He also was elected President of the Cheshire Agricultural Society for 1887.

One spin-off from all these horticultural interests was that he took action to reduce the amount of smoke emitted from the works chimneys which fouled the atmosphere and inhibited the growth of plants - an early example of a smoke abatement policy, which no doubt pleased the townsfolk, particularly on washing day!

Webb 5 ft 6 in. 2-4-2T No. 910 at Manchester (London Road).   *John Alsop Collection*

Webb 5 ft 6 in. 2-4-2T No. 2147 at Manchester (London Road).   *John Alsop Collection*

Chapter Nine

More Simples and Progress

Despite the bad reports given to the compounds rubbing off onto all Webb engines, this was an oversimplification of the state of the stock. Up to the mid-1890s the simples greatly outnumbered the compounds and did the vast majority of the revenue work, and they did this work reliably and relatively economically. Notwithstanding their relatively small size they were frequently coping, in later years, with 300 ton trains. Crewe boilers were tough and could be worked hard to produce the steam required, albeit at the expense of a heavy coal consumption. The compounds obtained for Frank a widespread reputation for his design expertise at a time when this technique was relatively new. This was good for the LNWR and him but the emphasis on compounds tended to push the simples into the background and relative obscurity despite their overwhelming numbers.

With the compounds being aimed first exclusively at the express services and only later the heavy freight roles, the remaining LNWR tasks were by no means neglected, for in 1890 a new 2-4-2T appeared, based on the 'Precursor'. In fact, the entire class of 'Precursors' were rebuilt to provide the core of the new tank class, which eventually totalled 160 locomotives by 1897.

Despite the 4-4-0 being the archetypal British passenger locomotive, widely used on express work, Webb seemed to have a fixation against that wheel arrangement, whereas it was his need to stick to light locomotives of relatively small size that produced his preference for the 2-4-0 layout. One other reason for keeping to small locomotives was the possibility of using already designed and proven components on a large number of newer designs. For example, the 2-4-0 'Precursor' parts built to 0-6-0 'DX' drawings were pistons, piston rods, crossheads, slide blocks, eccentric straps and sheaves, connecting rods, small and big end components. Likewise the 2-4-0 'Precedents', 5 ft express goods 0-6-0 and 0-6-2T shared a wide range of motion parts. This degree of standardization was very high indeed and contributed to the low final cost of Webb's engines. Whilst the compounds, with their massive middle cylinder, precluded any normal leading bogie, the other simple types could have been 4-4-0s in many cases. One can only speculate that perhaps it was a question of cost or the added complication of locating the inside cylinders to give adequate clearance that eliminated the consideration of a popular wheel arrangement. It has been suggested that he was, for some reason, distrustful of leading bogies, despite the large number of examples he had seen elsewhere, both at home and abroad, although this philosophy was to change somewhat at the end of his career, as we shall see.

A 2-4-0 was a compact layout and, so long as train weights and speeds remained reasonable, was adequate enough. Webb's answer to the need for more passenger locomotives was yet another 2-4-0, despite the trend to heavier train weights. This was an update of the 'Precedent class', with larger boiler and 6 ft 6 in. driving wheel. Originally known as 'Improved Precedent' they

'Improved Precedent' class 2-4-0 No. 1213 *The Queen* at Bletchley. *John Alsop Collection*

'Improved Precedent' class 2-4-0 No. 1485 *Smeaton* at Manchester (London Road).
John Alsop Collection

'Improved Precedent' class 2-4-0 No. 919 *Nasmyth* on a lengthy good train near Preston.
John Alsop Collection

'Improved Precedent' class 2-4-0 No. 271 *Minotaur* with a goods train at Chester.
John Alsop Collection

eventually were given the unofficial title 'Big Jumbo', the first example appearing in 1887. They took the names and numbers of the now obsolescent 'Newton' class 2-4-0s, and in fact incorporated some of the original parts, but could only be classed loosely as rebuilds. Coming shortly afterwards was a variant of this with 6 ft driving wheels, the 'Small Jumbo'. In all 166 of the former and 90 of the latter were turned out over the years until 1901. They were main line locomotives and almost immediately required double-heading on many of the express and semi-fast services allocated to them. The LNWR was beginning to suffer from the decades of Moon's small engine policy because the lightweight, and cheaper, track precluded larger, heavier, and more expensive locomotives. Parsimony in the past, although producing good returns for the investors, was now curtailing traffic growth for the future. Unfortunately, Frank was right in the firing line for many of the adverse comments, and had to start answering many critics.

Where Frank really scored in an engineering design sense was his sturdy structural design coupled to maximum interchangeability. This sturdiness meant that, as heavier train loads came along, the locomotives were capable of being driven hard to cope with the demands made of them without falling apart under the strain. The interchangeability ensured speedy replacement of worn parts by shed fitters from stocks of spares held for the purpose.

The 2-4-0s were a case in point, for Ramsbottom's design proved capable of being updated and improved at low cost with Webb's versions being merely a design variation of the original. He knew a good product when he saw it and Webb's versions of Ramsbottom's designs were essentially identical, and thus cost-effective, products. Moon may have been a good man in the financial and policy matters and was astute enough on production matters to realise that Webb was, with his designs, complying with his (Moon's) aspirations.

This philosophy also applied to the six-coupled designs which were largely based on the 'DX' 0-6-0.

Before leaving the 2-4-0s there is one interesting experiment carried out on No. 757 *Banshee*, built originally in 1863 as one of the Ramsbottom 'Samsons'. It was withdrawn in 1892 for conversion to yet another of Webb's schemes, that of friction drive. This dispensed with coupling rods and transmitted the drive from the leading, driven wheels, to the trailing driving wheels by means of a friction wheel. This could be raised or lowered by the driver as needed. The scheme was intended to combine the free-running qualities of the single driving wheel with the extra adhesion given by coupled wheels. For starting or climbing steep gradients the friction wheel would be raised to contact the front and rear wheels, making the locomotive effectively four-coupled, however, at speed on level or slight gradients the wheel would be lowered, turning the engine into a single driver. The experiment did not last long, probably due to excessive axle-box and tyre wear being caused by the fore and aft thrust on the axle-box and friction wheel tyre contact on the tyre. The locomotive lasted until 1896 in this form.

By the 1890s double-heading of the heaviest expresses became so commonplace that Frank took the 60-strong 'Problem' class of 2-2-2s and rebuilt them to act as pilot engines on these trains. They had already been reboilered with 140 psi units between 1879 and 1893, and the rebuilding in 1895 to 1899

The 'Problem' 2-2-2s lasted very long whilst Webb was around. No. 1 *Saracen* at Lichfield Trent Valley station in 1903.   *R.S. Carpenter Collection*

equipped them with 150 psi boilers and new frames. The 'Problems' were noted for their good speed capabilities and were also employed on light relief trains. It has often been wondered why these antiquated single-drivers, after all they were nearly 40 years old, were resurrected by Webb for continued use in the late 1890s. He had, of course, been leading draughtsman on their design and, as such, may have looked upon them as the first of his engines and they were, by now, becoming worn out. Frank clearly made a case for yet another rebuild to permit their continued use. The day of the single-driver was fast coming to a close as train weights increased. Although fast, free-running locomotives, their hauling power was restricted by the limited adhesion available. The relegation to these minor duties was a logical use for otherwise obsolete locomotives which, in their day, had been one of the premier express types on the LNWR.

For the more mundane shunting tasks in and around docks a batch of twenty 0-4-2STs was built in 1896. These employed a Bissel truck for the rear carrying wheels, to assist in rounding the tight curves that abounded in many docks' layouts. This eventually gave the class the name of 'Bissel Tanks'. They were notable for their square-shaped saddle tanks which extended the full length of the boiler/firebox/smoke box assembly and must have restricted the crew's forward vision considerably.

Some Webb designs were, at first sight, unorthodox. The two batches of 0-4-0Ts built for shunting work in 1880 (five) and 1882 (five) were a case in point. Firstly, they were oil-fired, with the driver and fireman being placed at opposite ends of the locomotive. The brake and reversing gear were operable from either end, so some teamwork was needed to ensure smooth operation. These peculiar little locomotives had 2 ft 6 in. diameter wheels driven by two 9 inch diameter and 12 in. stroke cylinders. The wheelbase was a mere 5 ft 6 in. which permitted

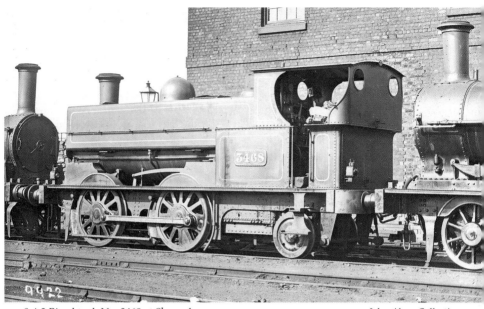

0-4-2 Bissel tank No. 3468 at Shrewsbury.   *John Alsop Collection*

This 0-4-2 Bissel tank survived at Buxton for many years. A 1933 photograph.
                                                             MRT/R.G. Jarvis Collection

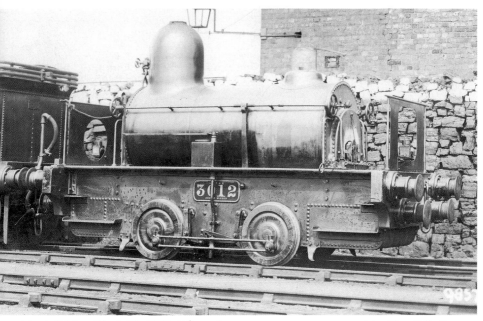

A basic 0-4-0 well tank, No. 3012 at Shrewsbury.   *John Alsop Collection*

0-4-0 well tank No. 3017 had 2 ft 6 in. wheels and is seen here at Crewe Works. It was fitted with a cab and bell for use in Liverpool docks.   *John Alsop Collection*

SIX WHEELS COUPLED SIDE-TANK PASSENGER LOCOMOTIVE, BUILT 1896.

Webb's large tank, the 0-6-2 'Watford' tank, built for the Watford-Euston suburban services.
Author's Collection

0-6-2 'Watford' tank No. 1563 at Euston.   *John Alsop Collection*

their use over the very tight curves which abounded around the works. Much of their duties being inside the works, no cab was fitted. The chimney was enclosed within the large dome, which all added up to a very unorthodox appearance. One final peculiarity unique to these locomotives was that some of them were fitted with an extra, lower, pair of buffers used for shunting chauldron wagons, still in use within the works confines in the latter decades of the 19th century. At least four of these small, but useful, locomotives lasted into LMS days.

For the next simple design Webb returned to the successful format produced by the 'Coal Tank', the 0-6-2T. In 1898, there appeared the first of the 'Watford Tanks' as they became known. Derived from the '18 inch Goods' 0-6-0 they were the first series of Webb designs to employ piston valves on a large scale, for out of the 80 eventually built, no fewer than 70 were so fitted.

Whilst all the above was taking place, in 1893 a new premium apprentice arrived at Crewe. This was 17-year-old Nigel Gresley, who came direct from Marlborough College, where he had recently won both Science and Form Prizes and wished to make a career in engineering. Gresley spent some time on the shop floor before being noticed by Webb and taken under his wing. Having completed his five years term he was then looking for some further experience and left for Horwich and the L&YR, being taken by Aspinall for a year's pupilage. Quite probably this Horwich position was encouraged by his Crewe apprenticeship, although whether Webb ever corresponded with Aspinall on this transfer is not known.

By 1894 there were 2,700 locomotives of the principal classes on the LNWR of which some 1,533 were Webb designs and nearly 1,200 either pure Ramsbottom or Webb-produced Ramsbottom designs and of these 60 (the 'Problems') were currently being rebuilt by Webb, so his hand was evident everywhere. However, on the passenger side, many of these classes were of the 2-4-0 layout with the 2-2-2-0 compounds carrying out the majority of important express duties. The goods traffic was catered for by 0-6-0s ranging from the 'Special DX' to the 'Cauliflower'. Tank engines, of 2-4-0 and 2-4-2 arrangements, numbered 340, plus 300 0-6-2 'Coal Tanks'. The LNWR was a small engine line but train weights were growing, and here we come to a point where Frank Webb had to go for something larger. Sir Richard Moon was no longer around and the constraints imposed by his rigid style of management were gone. The first of the 0-8-0 three-cylinder compounds were in production and the drawing office was busy preparing the drawings for the new 4-4-0 four-cylinder compounds which, it was hoped, would cope with sizeable increases in train weights - and speeds - in the case of passenger traffic.

However, as we shall see, the zenith of Frank's career had been reached. He had been in office for nearly a quarter of a century and his expertise was such that Euston and the Board readily accepted what he offered in the motive power sphere. After all, his locomotives were inexpensive, capable of hard use and, for the simples at least, utterly reliable. Crewe works was a competent and up-to-date facility wrought by his planning. With such an established expertise he was going to be difficult to unseat, his concern for the employees' conditions made him popular within the Locomotive Department and his community responsibilities and generosity gave him widespread recognition as a pillar of Crewe society.

The LNWR top management, however, had now changed for a new breed of Chairman, Lord Stalbridge, and General Manager, Frederick Harrison. The former enjoyed a relatively harmonious relationship with Webb, whilst the latter was soon set on a path of confrontation. A fuller appraisal of this will be found in Chapter Eleven. Webb clearly was steeped in his ways and no longer had the support of someone of the thinking of Richard Moon and, as a result, his strong beliefs in his own design aims over-rode the desires of his Running Department for larger, more powerful, locomotives. Not that he was incapable of overseeing the design of such engines, his skills as an engineer were still more than adequate enough. Over two decades of steady development had moulded his ways and his autocratic handling of Crewe's affairs had produced a way of thinking which could not, it seems, be altered much. So design matters which on some railways were to result in large locomotives did not get much consideration, particularly in the express passenger needs. Although the freight traffic was to be catered for by the advent of the eight-coupled compounds, the important income from that traffic was overshadowed by the prestige generated by the express services particularly those linking the major cities of England and Scotland.

As the 20th century approached, Frank turned his mind to his continued interest in electricity, though not so much as for lighting or factory power, for this was by now well established, but its application to trains. This latter aspect had a public airing at the Jubilee of the Crewe Mechanics Institute on 29th January, 1896, at which he said in his address: 'In 10 to 15 years from now trains moved by electricity will run from all the large centres of the country at a rate of speed which can hardly be realised, probably 100 mph'. He also mentioned in this speech that he would be quite happy to use electricity to power trains. Not long after this startling pronouncement he suggested to Lord Stalbridge, the new Chairman, that he be permitted to design and build a prototype electric train, but the idea was turned down. The lure of electric trains never left him, however, and he persisted in his wish to try out this new form of power. In 1902 he is recorded as having pointed out at an ICE meeting that he had in hand a complete and comprehensive scheme for the electrification of the LNWR, and a plan had also been prepared for its application to suburban services.

He was, despite a firm adherence to steam power, a firm believer in alternative power. This rebuttal of his progressive ideas was just one of many such instances to plague his final years in office. Frank was sensitive to such treatment and, probably due to his bachelor status, tended to keep matters to himself. He fully knew his capabilities and it must have been frustrating to have his schemes capped by those with little understanding of technological advances waiting to be implemented. Despite his advancing years, his mind was still active and he was able to look to the future and progress. However, the application of electricity in the works was by now so important that a department had been set up to manage it. To this department he sent his nephew William, Walter's son, as Electrical Assistant for the works. William had served his apprenticeship under his uncle between 1883 and 1888 and clearly shown promise in electrical matters to be given this responsibility.

We have seen that twice Frank courted ladies who attracted him, but to no avail. Clearly he was not a confirmed bachelor by choice, but his luck in the matrimonial sphere never took off. That he was quite happy with children around is instanced in the following story from the *Crewe Guardian*. The occasion was the preparation of a bust of himself by Sir Henry B. Robertson:

> When Mr Webb was on a visit to him, Sir Henry's children were playing with some wet clay. Mr Webb began to play with them. At length Sir Henry suggested that he should make a start on the model of Mr Webb. The latter agreed, and the work occupied some considerable time. Mr Webb would not sit for more than five minutes at a time and had a habit of going to sleep. At length, Sir Henry warned him that if he went to sleep again, he (Sir Henry) would go out for a walk. Suddenly Mr Webb appeared to be sleeping, Sir Henry left the room, and on returning he found that instead of going to sleep, Mr Webb had been busy on the bust. He had modelled two horns, one on each side of the head, and turned up the moustache, and pulled down the beard - the result being a remarkable likeness to Mephistopheles!

In this rare insight into his private life we see not only an affinity to the antics of children, but a wicked sense of humour.

The other interesting thing about this episode is that Sir Henry (knighted in 1890) was Frank's godson. This came about in 1862, when he was Works Manager at Crewe. Henry Robertson, Sir Henry's father, had settled in North Wales and formed the Brymbo Mineral Railway Company, which bought a local estate and ironworks. Following the completion of that railway, Robertson was involved in many other railway projects in the Midlands and Mid-Wales. How Frank became acquainted with him is not known, but clearly a close friendship grew between them resulting in the selection as godfather .

With Moon's departure from the scene the economic pressure was off, but Frank was, by now, so imbued with that philosophy it was not easy to adapt had he wished to do so. Lord Stalbridge had known Webb for some time and held a footplate pass which he used on frequent occasions. The rapport between the Chairman and CME occasioned by the pass had a side effect in one matter which led up to the final episodes in Frank's career at Crewe. This concerned the continued complaints made by Harrison (the new General Manager) and Turnbull (the Operating Superintendent) regarding the time they claimed was continually lost on the principal expresses hauled by the compounds. These complaints did not, however, come direct to Webb, but were directed to Stalbridge. This cannot have helped things in that Frank must have felt he was being passed over in matters of prime importance to him and that his reputation was at stake. Stalbridge must have regarded this apparent attack on Webb with some dismay, as his experience on footplate trips might have contradicted some of the criticisms and may well have played down any harsh judgements. This all took place as the first evidence of illness appeared in the background during the last year or so of Frank's service.

4-4-0 4-cylinder 'Jubilee' class No. 1901 *Jubilee* on a passenger train at Bushey.

John Alsop Collection

4-4-0 'Jubilee' class No. 1502 *Black Prince* in its original double chimney form.

John Alsop Collection

Chapter Ten

More Compounds

So far as the continuation of the compound story is concerned, there was a change in philosophy to come from 1896 after Webb had taken out two patents for four-cylinder compounds which employed a balanced concept involving the driving of one axle. Clearly it was no longer possible to do without coupling rods, so the locomotives became conventional 4-4-0s. With the smaller diameter of a pair of low pressure inside cylinders it was now possible to incorporate a leading bogie, although the end result was more a double-Bissel truck than a conventional bogie on swing-links. Another reason for a four-cylinder layout was that James Manson on the Glasgow & South Western Railway was building a four-cylinder simple design.

Manson was well advanced by the time the news filtered through, but Frank was not deterred by the lack of time implicit, for on 6th April, 1897 order No. E117 was issued for the supply of two four-cylinder 4-4-0s with 7 ft driving wheels. On the 20th June the first example was completed. The speed of design and construction could have been due to the fact that Frank wished to have his four-cylinder type on the rails before Manson. Whatever the reason, with the design being new this was clearly a magnificent effort by the drawing office and works, the former having been on overtime from the start. Notwithstanding the great effort to complete this new four-cylinder design, which was in fact a simple, within a few days the second example appeared, as a compound. So the drawing office had been well motivated, for this particular version had a double chimney and a special divided smoke box based on that tried out earlier on 2-4-0 No. 1532. The simple was No. 1501 *Iron Duke* and the compound No. 1502 *Black Prince*. They were subsequently renumbered 1901 and 1902 with No. 1901 being renamed *Jubilee* to commemorate Queen Victoria's Diamond Jubilee that year (1897). The name *Iron Duke* was transferred to the next compound built, No. 1903. It was this locomotive that was rostered for a special task arranged by Webb in 1899.

The Engineering Conference of the Institution of Civil Engineers was held in London in June of that year and it was arranged for a visit to Crewe works to be made on the 8th of that month. Some 200 of the delegates were conveyed to Crewe and back on a special train drawn by No. 1903, which dealt with the 340 ton load in fine form, covering the 159 miles there in 3 hours and 10 minutes. Frank himself conducted the party round part of the works, proudly showing off his latest creations. By this time the Crewe expertise was widely acknowledged as being of the best and renowned for its cost-effectiveness. Raw materials in and completed locomotives out was an example of manufacturing expertise par excellence. Pupils still came to learn their trades and many passed on to other railways throughout the World. See *Appendix One* for a summary of this aspect.

The compound showed considerable advantages over the simple and, despite the restrictions imposed by the two sets of valve gear arranged inside for driving all four valves, which meant that the cut-off for both high and low pressure cylinders was operated simultaneously, these locomotives were much

An unidentified 'Jubilee' 4-cylinder compound on an up express passing through Tamworth, *c.*1902-3.   *R.S. Carpenter Collection*

'Jubilee' class 4-4-0 No. 1918 *Renown*.   *John Alsop Collection*

better performers than the three-cylinder compounds which had preceded them. Another 38 were built, and when the sole simple variant was rebuilt as a compound, the class now named after this one, 'Jubilee', totalled 40. The example of this class which had the double chimney arrangement ran with this from 1897 until replaced by a standard single chimney arrangement and conventional smokebox in 1902.

Pleased with the much better performance of the four-cylinder layout, Webb kept to this format for all his future compounds. Another batch of 4-4-0 compounds then appeared, the 'Alfred the Great' class, which were broadly similar to the 'Jubilees', but employed a larger boiler and four sets of valve gear so that, if required, the low pressure cylinders could be independently controlled. Although the 'Jubilee' batch had shown better performance than the three-cylinder types, the inability to adjust the high and low pressure cut-offs independently did cramp their style somewhat. In September 1903, No. 1952 *Benbow*, of the second batch was modified with 'duplex' gear enabling completely independent high and low adjustments. This improved the overall performance considerably, and the change had been authorized by Webb in February 1903. By the end of 1907 all the second batch, the 'Alfred the Greats', had been so altered. These were the best of all Webb's passenger compounds and the last one to survive Grouping was not withdrawn until 1928 by Fowler.

This final change approved by Frank had a dramatic effect on the locomotive's performance and some notable runs were logged. One was of a 480 ton train from Rugby to Harrow in 80 minutes, which points to a sustained power output of around 1,000 cylinder horsepower. It seemed at last that Webb had found an acceptable compound design.

The redoubtable Rous-Marten gave the modified four-cylinder compound 4-4-0 a good report following his assessment of a trip reported in 1904. However, the credit for the improvements is often incorrectly given to George Whale for, although seeing to the implementation of this change, he did so on the basis of the original drawings approved by Webb. Whale already had plans to improve the class further by converting them to two-cylinder simples, a task easily done by removing the outside high-pressure cylinders and redesigning the steam passages. But this was to come in the future, after Webb's death.

The earlier express four-cylinder exercise showing much more promise, it was natural for Webb to introduce a variant of the earlier three-cylinder compound 0-8-0 with the same four-cylinder layout as the 'Alfred the Great', but resorting to the derived valve gear of the 'Jubilees'. Known as the 'B' class, the first of these appeared in 1901 and was followed by 169 more over the years. This design employed a larger boiler than the earlier type, some five inches greater in diameter and with a pressure of 200 lb. instead of 175 lb. Otherwise many of the other details were common to the three-cylinder variant. There were just two sets of motion for the four cylinders, the outside valves being driven from the inside valves by means of rocking arms concealed under covers reminiscent of the lid of a piano.

The derived motion was not too much of a disadvantage at the relatively low operating speeds. Many of these 0-8-0s lasted well into LMS days, 11 living out their lives as compounds with the rest being rebuilt as two-cylinder simples over the years.

L&N.W. FOUR-CYLINDER COMPOUND PASSENGER ENGINE, KING EDWARD VII.

'Alfred the Great' class 4-cylinder compound No. 1942 *King Edward VII*. The final express design of Webb. Some degree of rebuilding has taken place, for it has a Whale cab.

Author's Collection

'Alfred the Great' class 4-cylinder compound No. 1950 *Victorious* at Euston with its original cab.

John Alsop Collection

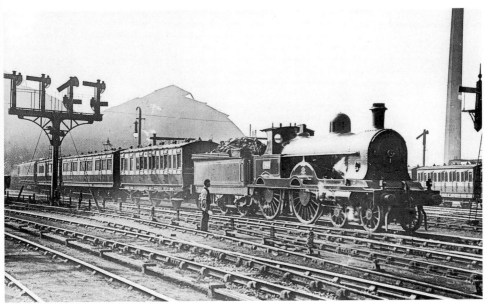

'Alfred the Great' class No. 1950 *Victorious* leaves Manchester (London Road) station with a passenger train.   *John Alsop Collection*

An unidentified 'Alfred the Great' class at speed with an up express on Bushey water troughs.
                                                                              John Alsop Collection

This view of 'B' class 0-8-0 4-cylinder compound No. 1881 emphasises the large front overhang.
Author's Collection

The fireman fills the tender of 'B' class 0-8-0 No. 1436.   *John Alsop Collection*

With the satisfactory performance of the four-cylinder compound 0-8-0s and 4-4-0s as a catalyst, Frank turned to the development of a locomotive for mixed-traffic duties, with the intended role of taking over from the 'Cauliflower' 0-6-0s. This final offering, in the compound story, to come from him was a 4-6-0, the first of this arrangement attributed to him. The new design was for mixed-traffic use and utilised the boiler and motion of the latest 0-8-0, with the high pressure cylinders of 15 in. from the original 16 in. The driving wheels were 5 ft 9 in. in diameter which made them rather small for the true mixed-traffic role, which was more associated with fast goods and passenger work. The first example, No. 1400, was turned out at Crewe in March 1903, not long before Frank was eventually to retire. A second example appeared in June of that year and the balance of 28 came out in three batches in November-December 1903 (8), September-October 1904 (10), and January-February 1905 (10). Many of these new compounds took the names and numbers of 'Experiment' and 'Dreadnought' three-cylinder compounds then being withdrawn by Webb's successor. They eventually became known as the 'Bill Bailey' class and were undistinguished performers, being confined to relatively short lives before scrapping. Frank's continued inward looking philosophy and set ways still failed to grasp the simple answers that others would have applied to solve problems that beset some of his designs. His lifelong refusal to become involved in discussions with his equals on other railways, particularly those involved with the ARLE, shut him off from answers to problems which could have eased his task. Clearly, one is led to believe that his egotistical outlook had a lot to do with that attitude. The more he got involved in the compound story, the more he seemed to take considerable time to implement the design improvements that were eventually made. In his final decade as CME the vast majority of his efforts in the locomotive sphere were biased towards compound designs and, whilst the odd simple design appeared, little attempt seemed to be made to refine them into future large locomotives. The few that did appear were ignored in the interests of compound continuation. Outsiders watched and noted the struggle to produce good performers and saw problems appearing. The British acceptance of the compound principle was severely dented by Webb's apparent failures. So long as there were ample supplies of cheap quality coal available there seemed little point in producing more complex locomotives which gave relatively small fuel savings at the expense of the risk of greater maintenance costs and first costs.

By now, despite the more acceptable 0-8-0 and 4-4-0 four-cylinder variants, the adverse reports on the Webb compounds as a whole were giving that type of locomotive a bad name in the UK, with many CMEs openly hostile to their introduction. This fact was reinforced by the accelerating withdrawal for scrapping of the earlier three-cylinder compounds, some of which were barely 10 or 12 years old. Whilst Webb was clearly very highly regarded as a locomotive engineer these CMEs felt that his stubborn resolve to utilise compounding was producing poor performers and was a technique to be avoided. There were the odd exceptions, Worsdell on the GER and NER respectively produced some good compounds, albeit two-cylindered. However, Worsdell was also engaged in trials of a three-cylinder compound, with the single high pressure cylinder layout, rebuilt from one of his two-cylinder compounds. The design of this had been under the direction of Walter Smith, his chief draughtsman, who later was to

'B' class 0-8-0 No. 1890 at Shrewsbury.   *John Alsop Collection*

'B' class 0-8-0 No. 1891 at Carlisle Upperby.   *John Alsop Collection*

An unidentified 4-6-0 'Bill Bailey' class with a passenger train.   *John Alsop Collection*

'Bill Bailey' class 4-6-0 No. 1352.   *John Alsop Collection*

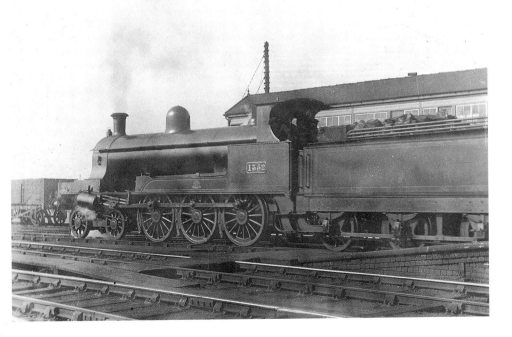

influence Johnson on the MR at Derby into designing such a type, which was eventually to become the famed Midland Compound.

Bowman Malcolm of the Belfast & Northern Counties Railway in Ireland stuck rigidly to the compound theme over many years, but preferred the two-cylindered approach, along the Worsdell-Von Borries concept. Churchward was beginning to consider compounding on the GWR but taking his time in giving it a trial. This he did in the early years of the 20th century by buying in some French 4-4-2 four-cylinder compounds for comparison with his own two-cylinder simple 4-6-0s.

And here we find a fundamental feature of Webb's design philosophy surfacing. Whereas Churchward was open to ideas from outside, and adopting them where he could see distinct advantages, Webb pursued his path of in-house developments for everything. Other designs may be offering good performance and reliability but his designs, in his eyes, were superior - and cheaper. This continual pressure to hold back on costs was, in many respects, a driver for his approach to all design matters. By the time Moon had gone Frank was so imbued with the need to economise that it was difficult, even when building bigger locomotives, for him not to apply the need for economy in production and operation. Moon's parsimonious approach had produced lightweight track which resulted in restricted axle loading and thereby small locomotives which were cheap to build. Likewise, the speed restrictions imposed by Moon led to economic costs of operation and maintenance of the whole track work and stock. To break out of that mould was difficult until the root constraints had been effectively removed and so, the net effect was that Webb could not have produced larger, heavier, locomotives even if he had so wished whilst Moon was in office.

Throughout Frank's career we have found the economy of production coming to the fore. Sometimes he would try out a beneficial feature which might offer a small improvement in overall performance of a design only to ignore it in future derivative designs. In other words, if an 'improvement' only produced a small saving in operating cost, that saving over the life of the locomotive being insufficient to cover the cost of designing, making and servicing the part in question, then we find that 'improvement' discarded.

'Bill Bailey' class 4-6-0 No. 1400 with a cattle train at Old Colwyn.   *John Alsop Collection*

Chapter Eleven

The Final Days and Retirement

With Moon retired from the scene, a major shift at the top was inevitable and a dynamic new personality awaited in the wings for inevitable promotion. This was one Frederick Harrison, soon to be the new General Manager.

Whilst Sir George Findlay was General Manager there had been little collaboration, but no marked animosity between him and Webb. Both were very ambitious men and autocratic in their ways. One big difference in the way they planned their careers was the matter of ensuring a successor was in place to take over at very short notice. Whilst Webb ignored that factor, Findlay started a train of events very early in his tenure of high office on the LNWR for, when he was appointed as General Goods Manager by Moon, he gathered a core staff around him. In this small group was Frederick Harrison, a clerk from Shrewsbury who was determined to climb the ladder of promotion.

Findlay noted Harrison's abilities and made sure that he was given every opportunity to spread his wings over seven years before promoting him to the position of Assistant District Superintendent at Liverpool, followed by a year at Chester in the same capacity. Harrison was only 31 when a further promotion, to Assistant Superintendent of the Line came. He spent 10 years in that position before a further promotion, to Chief Goods Manager, resulted in him being directly responsible to Findlay and perfectly placed for the ultimate move into the General Manager's office. This came in March 1893 with the sudden death of Sir George Findlay. Harrison slipped effortlessly into the General Managership and immediately started to implement changes. In Moon's days economy had been a main driver, which had resulted in a lack of improvements in amenities and operating standards. In the early 1890s the LNWR was beginning to slip behind in the trend to speed up services and its competitive edge was being eroded. Matters were now set for a change, Harrison being in favour of corridor stock and the speeding up of services in addition to considerable improvements to the line in order to cope with the increasing passenger and freight traffic.

It is around this time that we find Frank Webb falling behind in what should have been expected of him. But his views on Harrison were already rigidly fixed, as we shall see, and he stubbornly continued in his own way of dealing with his own interpretation of traffic needs. Much of the ensuing shortfalls in locomotive performance, more particularly for express passenger services, resulted from this attitude, and he was never to have Harrison up to Crewe. Doubtless Harrison would have liked to unseat Webb, but the Locomotive Superintendent was so well entrenched and popular at Crewe, this would only have resulted in much acrimony to the detriment of the railway. The 'Hire and Fire' management philosophy was yet to emerge in the UK. It was, therefore, inevitable that matters associated with locomotive development deteriorated and gave Webb a bad reputation as an engineer. This only happened at the close of what was to be a great career, but in the many assessments of Webb's design career it has been made a major criticism encompassing the remarkably good earlier days as well.

However, we have seen that Webb had launched into what had been needed for some years now, the production of, by LNWR standards, larger locomotives. Matters, however, were not going all that smoothly. Compounds were, apart from the 'Teutonics' and the new four-cylinder 4-4-0s coming along, still relatively poor performers and attracting a lot of adverse comments as to their overall capabilities. Quite often they would have to be given pilot engines to cope with the ever-increasing train weights as bogie stock began to be introduced on a wider scale. It was clear that something needed to be done. Webb still hankered after his compound philosophy and could not be persuaded to consider changing his ways, least of all by Frederick Harrison, with whom he never got on. The attitude of Harrison hardly helped matters. The new General Manager wished to have much more say over what went on at Crewe in the design and production aspects, but was firmly blocked by Frank, who would not tolerate any incursion into his empire. The additional pressures placed on him, at a time when age was beginning to tell, must have added quite considerably to his worries and may well have affected his judgement at times. But then, even if they did realise this, those under him would have held their thoughts to themselves for fear of precipitating their removal, or even, dismissal. On top of this, there were those who would not baulk at undermining Webb by siding with Harrison, for they could sense promotion ahead. The politics of this, combined with a general move in industry for newer, more open, methods of management started to move affairs with Harrison who, to all intents and purposes, declared war on Webb.

This 1894 photograph shows all the chief officers of the LNWR. Webb is seated with the drawing on his lap, slightly left of centre.   *E. Talbot Collection*

This could not have helped a man in his sixties who was expected to have an answer to all problems put his way. At this stage it is difficult to gauge exactly how the immense pressures, which clearly were there, affected Frank. Subsequent events tend to show that they weighed on his mind, making him even more resolved to carry on in his own way - after all, he had been in charge for over a quarter of a century now and should know what to do. As time progressed to the early 20th century he was old enough to retire gracefully and see his responsibilities passed on to a successor, but there was no one being positioned for such an event by this time.

Harrison had visited the USA in 1896 to study the railway management methods over there and came back with a desire to change the LNWR management structure methods to those developed in that country. Any mention of this to Webb was met with complete disdain, he had no intention of changing his ways - not ever. A typical remark attributed to him was: 'I will not be told my business by a jumped-up clerk!'

Harrison and Webb sized each other up, with the former clearly dissatisfied with the size of Webb's remuneration, which was by then £7,000 per year [about £750,000 in today's money]. Harrison accordingly began to draw to himself certain key people, notably Robert Turnbull, the Superintendent of the Line, and George Whale, who was in Webb's Department as Running Superintendent. Whale, whom it is recorded did not see eye-to-eye with Webb, most certainly had problems with Frank over the troubles with the three-cylinder express compounds and, the longer he was fobbed off by a stubborn CME, the more he was determined that they should be withdrawn as soon as practicable, should he ever get to a position from which he could achieve this. Events after Frank's retirement, with Whale as CME, enabled this to be implemented within a fairly short time. Harrison, in fact, was never to visit Crewe whilst Webb was in office, so acrimonious was the feeling between them, but this was to be remedied within a few weeks of his departure. One particular event which aroused much bad feeling was in 1901 when Harrison imposed the 'equals 17' rule on the Locomotive Department. Basically, this meant that every passenger train which exceeded 270 tons tare weight was to be double-headed, with no account taken of booked time, gradients encountered or engine class. Frank must have been very annoyed at this intrusion by a dictatorial General Manager, particularly as many of the later compounds, when handled by experienced crews, had shown themselves capable of dealing with train weights above the 270 ton limit.

There has been much intense speculation as to the medical condition which led to Frank Webb's retirement, much of it questionable. A particularly damning statement appeared in the *Engineer* of the 8th June, 1906, viz.

Mr Webb's temperament was peculiar, and he was not fortunate to have many friends. He never married and there is little doubt that a fear of the disease to which in the end he succumbed overshadowed his life...

The above statement is open to misinterpretation in a variety of ways. 'A peculiar temperament' can be construed by reference to some stormy moments at the office when stubborn determination to have it his way raised its head. His health was not all that good in his final years and could well have led to some irritable moments - perfectly understandable, particularly when it is remembered that Webb, for many years, was an important figure in and around Crewe and the County of Cheshire and had been used to having things his own way. But then, of course, he was in good health. In those days he would have had a good many friends, particularly in high places through his involvement in local affairs.

'He never married...' - Frank's bachelor status was nothing new, many other people, his brothers Arthur and William included, chose that way of life. The mention of this fact in the same sentence as the 'disease to which in the end he succumbed' is unfortunately too vague and has been used to link the remote possibility of mental problems in some earlier branch of the family resurfacing. Although where this notion came from is a mystery and, with his change in temperament due to the onset of the health breakdown which surfaced, much play appeared to be made of this fact to explain matters.

Peritonitis has been mentioned as a major contributor to Webb's condition in his last years and, if that was the illness which plagued his last days, can often be associated with the worry of overwork. His workload had been high for many years and it says much for his constitution that he was able to bear this for so long. But, obviously, the extreme discomfort brought about could well have been alleviated following his retirement, hence the three years between that and his eventual death seems logical. Frank Webb simply appears to have been worn out both physically and mentally by his 32 years of extreme and multiple responsibilities.

However, despite the onset of some illness Frank still showed himself to be well on top of developments. For example, June 1900 marked the outshopping of the 4,000th locomotive at Crewe. This was arranged to be 4-4-0 compound No. 1926 *La France*. It had been so named as it was to be sent to the Paris Exhibition of that year. Frank made sure that a French-speaking premium apprentice accompanied the brand-new and specially finished engine. In parallel with this event Frank received the freedom of the town by Crewe Council, clearly the 'Intimidation' affair had by now been forgotten and relations between Crewe and the works were back to normal. Also, in 1901, Frank had been associated with Crewe for 50 years and in recognition of this he presented a loving-cup to the town.

It seems reasonable at this stage to take a brief look at his last few months at work to try and assess his physical and mental condition during these last days in office.

July 1902 found him ordering that his coupé be available to transport the Prime Minister of Uganda, Apolo Kagma, and his party around the works on an official visit. A photograph taken at the time shows Webb completely at ease, leaning nonchalantly on a buffer of the coupé. No signs of any affliction here, or was it just a good day? The coupé consisted of an old Trevithick 2-2-2 coupled to a 6-wheeled carriage, the forward part of which comprised a tender unit and the rearmost two-thirds took the form of a comfortable saloon seating up to 10 in comfort.

In November 1902 Webb told the LNWR Board that he would have to retire soon. This was reported in the *Engineer* of November 28th thus:

The Prime Minister of Uganda, Apolo Kagma, visited Crewe works in July 1902 and arrived in Webb's private coupé. FWW leaning against the buffer looks quite relaxed.

Author's Collection

After 52 years of hard work Mr F.W. Webb has suggested to his directors that he is desirous of retiring from the position of Chief Mechanical Engineer of the LNWR. But the date of his withdrawal from active service has not been fixed, nor has the name of his successor been mentioned.

Although not mentioned in that report, his health was probably the root cause of that decision. There were several key people around capable of taking over and the Board, taking note of Frank's comment, began to discuss possible candidates, but no immediate decision appeared to have been taken. Some references have indicated that Aspinall was in Frank's mind as a potential successor, but by this date he had been fully installed as General Manager of the L&YR for over three years. However, Frank must have been mollified to some degree by the knowledge that old pupil Hoy was now Locomotive Superintendent of that railway in place of Aspinall. Doubtless Aspinall might have been prised away from the L&YR by a big enough offer of salary, but this would not have fitted in with Harrison's determination to reduce the CME's salary considerably when a change became inevitable.

Around this time there came a significant comment from the LNWR Board that:

... having desired to be relieved from the duties of Chief Mechanical Engineer, the Directors wish to record their very great appreciation of the devoted and exceptional services he has rendered to the company since his appointment in 1871.

So far as locomotive design matters were concerned, for the compound 4-4-0s, two important features were to be introduced in 1903. These were, firstly, the alteration of the valve gear to permit independent cut-offs as mentioned in the previous chapter and, secondly, the reboiling of two examples with units having Belpaire fireboxes.

This group of visitors hail from India. The gentleman seated at the front is His Highness the Ilahore Saheb of Morbi.   *Author's Collection*

As 1903 advanced he was involved in many outside matters requiring his presence. Firstly came the annual meetings of the Cottage Hospital and the Mechanics Institute in February, followed by the opening of an Exhibition of Arts and Crafts at the Town Hall. Then he was to be found again at the Mechanics Institute in March at the annual prize-giving ceremony. He spoke that evening during the proceedings, winding up with the comment: '... that we may all meet here again next year'. This seems a little strange, for it was by now very common knowledge that a change was coming at the top and that Mr Webb would be retiring soon. It was as though he could not imagine that by then he would be retired and probably away from Crewe.

To further his growing interest in the motor-car as a personal transport medium, Frank ordered a new model from the Maudslay Company for his forthcoming retirement. The cost was 900 guineas (not far short of £100,000 at today's values). But it is doubtful that he was ever able to take advantage of this acquisition after the events of the following few months.

In April 1903 the Mechanics Institute had a new physics laboratory opened, with Webb present to carry out the brief ceremony. A few days later, on the 22nd, matters took a decisive step with the official release of the name of Frank's successor. It was to be George Whale, who up to then had been the Running Superintendent. Whether or not this appointment was connected with the erratic performance of some of the compounds, which were struggling to keep time on some trains, is not immediately clear, but a running man should certainly have a clear insight into what was needed to remedy the situation. Also, Whale was, we have seen, well in with Harrison.

Matters were, by this time, moving at an increased pace. Webb was definitely off-colour by now, and clearly was a sick man. He managed to attend the annual dinner of the Past and Present Crewe Association on the 5th May. This must have been quite an effort for him, as it involved travelling down to London for the event.

Whale was already deputising for Frank quite often now and started signing drawings on the 25th May. Three days previously Webb had made his last Will and most certainly his condition was worrying him - and others, who noticed a sharp increase in irritability, which had been evident in the last few months, An example was noted by George Whale and, in later years, described to old pupil Henry Ivatt during a private dinner engagement at Chester Place. Apparently Webb was shown a drawing which he appeared to find fault with. He ran a pencil over it, presumably over the relevant part which annoyed him and then proceeded to rip it up. The pieces were then thrown on the floor and stamped upon. Unfortunately, all this was in the presence of several staff. Whale could not stomach this extreme behaviour and its effect upon the morale of the staff and shortly afterwards departed for Euston to report to the Board that matters could not proceed any longer with this sort of example being set by Webb. In this extreme action he had the backing of Trevithick, the Assistant Manager of the locomotive works, and Bowen Cooke, the new Running Superintendent. But before any hard and fast action could be taken by the Board, events at Crewe moved fast, precipitating the removal of Webb from office. It must have been just after Whale's representation that a further incident involving his deputy chief clerk, W. Horabin, resulted in a messenger being sent to Webb's brother, Canon Arthur Webb, at St Paul's Vicarage nearby. Arthur immediately came to the works and managed to persuade Frank to go home. He never set foot inside the works again and any decision of the Board resulting from Whale's plea was most certainly made redundant.

The *Crewe Chronicle* for 30th May, 1903 carried a report which stated that Frank Webb had been taken seriously ill and was now recovering at Colwyn Bay.

The final decline had been very swift, the signs of a quite serious illness were all there, yet Frank seemed determined to go the full 12 months of notice as stipulated and clearly at the end was pushing himself too hard. His management style and philosophy demanded that *all* decisions likely to affect locomotive stock and its use on the LNWR were his ultimate responsibility. The pressure of work overcame his capabilities as age and illness asserted their presence. Had he married, the steadying influence of a wife would have quite probably led to a different state of events and retirement may well have been a much easier option.

The time at Colwyn Bay was for complete rest and recuperation; away from Crewe and the pressures of work, Frank was able to make a slow recovery. After some time there he was transferred, probably for a final assessment, to Coton Hill Mental Hospital where he underwent final observation and treatment. Here his recovery obviously continued, with Dr Atkinson being kept informed as to the progress of the clearly debilitating illness which had caused the breakdown.

By now, the technical press had got hold of some reports of his condition, but the early reports they produced were put quite mildly. The example from the *Railway Engineer* stated:

All our readers will regret to learn that Mr F.W. Webb's health has failed him to such an extent that he has been obliged to hand over the onerous duties attaching to the position of Chief Mechanical Engineer of the London & North Western Railway to his appointed successor, Mr G.Whale, somewhat sooner than was arranged. We are sure everyone will unite with us in hoping Mr Webb will soon recover his health, so that he may enjoy the retirement he has so fully earned.

After a short time recuperating at Coton Hill Webb was deemed recovered enough to be discharged. It seemed that he had now accepted that his working days were over. As Chester Place was to be handed on to George Whale and it was not advisable to return to Crewe, a house, 'The Red Lodge' in Parsonage Road, Bournemouth, was bought and he removed down there, being accompanied by Dr Atkinson, who saw him safely installed. With medical care arranged for his continual well-being, Frank lived on there quietly, amongst a collection of his personal effects which had been brought from Stanway Manor, to which he would never return.

With all the rearranging of his life, Frank missed the unveiling of the Crewe South African War Memorial, built as the Crewe Reservist's Memorial erected in Queen's Park on 8th August, 1903. The base of the monument, which commemorated the fact that three men from Crewe were killed in action, originally had a bronze model of a Webb locomotive, compound *King Edward VII*, incorporated into it.

One feature of Crewe works' capabilities following Frank's retirement was the change in top management. In the Webb era the CME had overall control over the works management and every order was assiduously followed up to see that matters proceeded according to plan. On Frank's departure, Whale immediately delegated much responsibility to a new, and relatively inexperienced, management team of A.R. Trevithick and J. Homfray. Both were ex-running men and had little or no works management backgrounds. Whale clearly wished to remove the Webb philosophy at that level and institute his own ways of tackling problems. In fact, this positioning of new brooms led to a bit of a crisis in 1904-5 when Trevithick all too enthusiastically followed orders to scrap the three-cylinder compounds. The result was a locomotive shortage which gave the LNWR quite severe problems until replacement stock became available. The ensuing events caused the Board to see to it that Trevithick never attained the CME position that could well have come his way. Frank had not yet passed on but, if he had been aware of this happening, was clearly well out of the loop in retirement at Bournemouth.

With what turned out to be more of a final accolade than a firm appointment, the Institution of Civil Engineers had elected Frank as a Senior Vice-President at their Annual General Meeting in 1903. Parallel to this ICE award he was also appointed a member of the Royal Commission to represent the country at the forthcoming St Louis International Exhibition. Neither of these prestigious appointments were ever taken up, his health being fragile to say the least. The Royal Commission could have produced some form of honour, maybe even a Knighthood, but it was not to be. No retirement recognition for him, even though something along these lines was richly deserved.

The comfortable environment at Bournemouth had a beneficial effect on his health, and he settled into the simple routine of retirement. He kept in touch with Dr Atkinson, who clearly was concerned at the condition of his old friend. However, his health never fully recovered and for nearly three years he lived on until his death on 4th June, 1906, in his 71st year. The death certificate records 'Malignant Disease of the Peritoneum' as the cause of death, with a note stating that it had been present for some six months.

The Webb Orphanage in original condition.

Apart from family and a few close friends, plus representation from Crewe and the Institutions of which he had been a member, the funeral was a small affair. Whale was not there, he sent A.R. Trevithick to represent him. Frank had made his Will back in 1903, as though he knew something was going to happen fairly soon. It is from the examination of the bequests that we get a feel for his deep humanity and how deeply he was integrated with the town of Crewe. Out of the total of £211,000 in his estate he left £10,000 to found a nursing institution to give free attendance for those in Crewe unable to afford such care; £9,000 for a number of church purposes in the town; £5,000 to Dr Atkinson and £3,000 to A.G. Hill his solicitor, both of Crewe. Other bequests included £5,000 to his good friend G.R. Jebb from Birmingham; £5,000 to his godson, Henry Robertson of bust fame. His surviving brothers Canon A.H. and Colonel W.G. Webb each received £30,000. He endowed a bed at University College hospital; sums of £1,000 went to the men's convalescent home at Rhyl, the Railway Servant's Orphanage at Derby, the Devonshire and Buxton Bath charity and the Manchester Royal Eye Hospital; £2,000 each to University College, Liverpool and Owens College, Manchester to found scholarships for LNWR employees and their sons. The sum of £1,000 went to the Institution of Mechanical Engineers for Webb prizes for railway engineering papers. An amount of £500 was allocated for the Royal Albert Asylum for idiots and imbeciles at Lancaster. He also remembered his chief clerk George Ellis and deputy chief clerk W. Horabin with sums of £300 and £200 respectively. The residue of the estate, which totalled some £70,000, was left to found the Webb Orphanage at Crewe for the children of deceased LNWR employees. This latter was opened at the end of 1911.

Crewe could not forget one of its most eminent engineers and, in later years, a Frank Webb Avenue was named in the town to carry forward the memory of a great benefactor. All this shows a great generosity towards all the institutions and professions that Webb thought worthy servants of society, as well as close friends and relatives. Intransigent and, towards the end of his days, irascible he may have been, but these did not take away his basic human decency and sense of civic responsibility.

Chapter Twelve

The Legacy

With the departure of Frank Webb, the almost continual development of Crewe works, which had been a central driver in his command of things, came to a halt and matters stagnated, never again to become a main priority with the CME. For Whale, good engineer that he was, was unable to appreciate the facts and figures associated with the cost control and efficiency of the works and locomotive departments. The interest in these matters died with Webb's departure. This situation was to remain for the rest of the days of the LNWR, and was only to be rectified in the days of the LMS. It was a shame that this was allowed to happen, for whilst Webb had been in charge the works had been kept an efficient organization under his strict control. Apart from engineering matters of design and production, Frank had made it his duty to keep watching briefs on investment matters, both charges and returns, expenditure on raw materials and stocks in hand of parts and materials. The all-important contribution of the locomotive department to the prosperity of the company had also been closely monitored. Interest in all these vital ingredients of an efficient, cost-effective concern died and Crewe works failed to advance year by year as fast as in Webb's days.

It says much for the legacy of Webb's organizational skills which had been established that Crewe was able to maintain a steady output of new and repaired stock, albeit in the face of a sudden inroad of withdrawals, primarily of three-cylinder compounds and 'Problems', instigated by the new Works Manager, A.R. Trevithick. This fierce attack was so sudden and uncoordinated with the output that the severe motive power shortage previously mentioned ensued, a matter which would never have been allowed to happen under Frank. Basically, the compounds had been overwhelmed by considerable increases in train weights and the 'Problems' were kept in service too long because Frank was rather fond of them. After all they represented his first major foray into design and, as such, had a rather sentimental value in his eyes.

Another fact which was to colour the LNWR locomotive development scene was the lack of interest shown by Whale in some design matters. This was at a time when there was a revolution in locomotive size and performance entering the scene on some other railways (such as the GWR). Initially, design philosophy still tended to be based on the long-standing Webb edicts and Crewe began to fall behind other railways' products. The modern progressive outlook needed to match these new developments, larger locomotives, superheating, Walschaerts valve gear, etc., had tended to be ignored or delayed until they absolutely had to appear, as they cut across the standardization issues so firmly rooted at Crewe. The absence of a strong leader such as Webb, with his continual interest in all matters, was very soon to have detrimental effect on matters of design and production.

One further criticism of Frank Webb's final years is that he had failed to have selected and advised anyone to be his successor. It would have been a hard act to follow and perhaps he felt that no one around who could match his experience; after all he did have a high opinion of his own talents. If someone of the calibre of Moon had still been around as Chairman things might have gone along a different path, for Webb and he had always got on and respected each other's abilities and judgements.

However, it is significant that, in the run up to his enforced retirement, Webb had allowed Whale to deputise for him in some matters, and this, by force of circumstances, had expanded into the design aspects. Whether or not this had been the beginning of a hand-over, is not clear, but the realisation that his time as CME was clearly limited may well have influenced matters. It seems unlikely that Webb would wish to leave an empty void when he did retire. So much in a derogatory sense has been heaped upon him following his retirement and death, that the true story of his undoubted management, organizational and design skills has been overshadowed by the reporting of all the negative events to the detriment. One hundred years ago, just as for today, it is the sensational news which takes precedence over the positive features of an eminent figure. Clearly, the rapport between the CME and top management was not as it had been up to 1891, which probably explains the lack of any countermanding statements.

Yet, in other matters relevant to the locomotive affairs, the LNWR still stood aloof from external bodies. For example a close association with the ARLE was not to be implemented until November 1908 when Bowen Cooke, who was to become CME the following year in place of Whale, was elected to represent the LNWR in a full capacity at last. Even when in 1904 the ARLE circulated an enquiry form regarding enginemen's retirement ages to all the railways, a stony silence emanated from the LNWR. Clearly the Webb influence had rubbed off on Whale.

Following his sudden departure, enforced retirement away from Crewe and subsequent death, the results of Frank Webb's career on the LNWR lived on for many years. To the layman the new locomotives remained larger editions of Webb types, for many of the changes made by his successors were not immediately visible. Crewe works still had the same outlook, production methods and a solid core of middle management steeped in the ways carefully nurtured over the 32 years of his incumbency. However, the 20th century and its new approach to industrial methodology and relations would eventually change these features, culminating in the effects of World War I and the subsequent Grouping of the British railway companies. Had he lived to see that, Frank Webb would have been horrified at the seemingly ruthless sweeping away of his long-established precepts, but that was all part of progress which needed attention in its application, attention beyond the grasp of many of his contemporaries. But, ironically, a new breed of managing engineers was coming along, many of whom had picked up their skill under Webb, for *that* was the real contribution made by this capable, generous and forthright person to the railway scene in this era of change.

So it was that the legacy of Webb's expertise lived on in the many famous engineers who had come under his guidance during their apprenticeship or pupilship, a legacy which served the railway scene in many other countries as well as in the United Kingdom. Compounds, however, were never to have the acceptance elsewhere, only being used in some considerable numbers by the Midland Railway under Fowler. But it is all too easy to forget that the majority of Webb locomotives were simples of considerable longevity which served the LNWR reliably for many years. They were the ones which ensured the continued prosperity and growth of the railway and, additionally, the enterprise forged at Crewe works had become a Mecca of industrial expertise second to none. All under the guidance of Frank Webb, a great railway engineering giant of Victorian days.

Appendix One

Famous Pupils of Webb

Name	Dates	Ultimate position
J.A.F. Aspinall	(1868-72)	CME GS&WR, CME and Gen. Manager L&YR
H.A. Ivatt	(1868-72)	CME GS&WR, then CME GNR
R. Atkinson	(1870-73)	Superintendent Rolling Stock, Canadian Pacific Railway
H.A. Hoy	(1872-77)	CME L&YR
E. Worthington	(1875-78)	Secretary, IMechE
F.C. Lea	(1878-80)	Professor Mech. Eng., Sheffield University
G. Hughes	(1882-87)	CME L&YR then CME LMS
T. Otway-Ruthven	(1889-93)	CME Nigerian Government Railway
F.R. Collins	(1890-94)	CME South African Railways
H.N. Gresley	(1893-98)	CME GNR then CME LNER
D. Fraser	(1895-97)	Locomotive Superintendent, Canton-Hankow Railway
E.A. Robinson	(1890s)	Managing Director, The Superheater Co.
J.G.B. Sams	(1897-1902)	Locomotive Superintendent, Jamaica Government Railway
H.F. Cardew	(1890s)	CME The Nizam's Railway
R.E. Bury	(1897-1902)	CME Mysore State Railway
A.W.Sutherland-Graeme	(1898-1903)	CME Federated Malay State Railway

Webb's pupils were well-chosen and advised by their mentor, as witness the large number of them to reach top positions elsewhere. Of those listed above only one managed to hold sway over Crewe, and then only for a brief three years from the distant realms of Horwich, this being George Hughes during his final years when CME of the LMS. The Crewe influence was spread to a total of four British and one Irish railways, plus many of the railways throughout the British Empire and elsewhere.

Clearly, Webb's advice to these pupils during their time under him, mixed with the experience gained from responsible tasks allotted to them, built a strong desire to be determined to succeed in the positions found for them away from Crewe. The LNWR could never have provided enough positions warranting their obviously outstanding capabilities. Webb clearly recognised this and, as in the case of John Aspinall that we have already seen in Chapter Four, would keep his ears to the ground to learn of suitable openings. His own expertise and wide circle of contacts throughout the railway world made sure of that. He took great pleasure in seeing many of these placings blossom and thereby spread the 'Crewe' ways to become almost a legend throughout the railway fraternity.

This, perhaps, was the greatest task that Webb carried out in his long career, for it was to have a long-lasting effect upon railway technologies in many countries throughout the World. He clearly recognised this, as he was always willing to find time to meet with his old pupils and share his views on many railway and engineering matters likely to be of interest to them.

Whitworth Scholars and Exhibitioners

Particularly during Webb's time, Crewe was noted for the large number of Whitworth Scholars and Exhibitioners to come from the ranks of all apprentices and pupils. To gain such an honour indicated a high standard of training, both practical and theoretical, which Webb clearly encouraged. Many of these scholars were to go on and achieve high positions elsewhere after their apprenticeship and early experience at Crewe. Of those who stayed with the LNWR, their fortunes could be mixed, a few rising only to the level of foreman, with the remainder getting as far as the responsibilities of middle management. They formed a good core of capable and reliable key staff for many years. Quite often Webb would have a gathering at Chester Place to hear about their progress, particularly from those who had left Crewe. His interest in old pupils and apprentices was legendary, it clearly pleased him to learn how *his* boys had measured up out in the railway industry as a whole.

Appendix Two

The Webb/Moon Relationship

This Appendix, at the risk of repeating some of the comments already made in the main text is to record the important relationship between Frank Webb and Sir Richard Moon and its ramifications on the locomotive developments of the LNWR.

One feature of the LNWR which undoubtedly influenced Webb in his position at Crewe was that of Sir Richard Moon's attention to the ratio of net revenue to working expenditure. This ensured that not only could a sizeable dividend, never less than 5 per cent, be paid to shareholders but that there was always plenty of capital available to be ploughed back into the railway. It was this capital that provided the finances needed to expand Crewe works, set up the in-house signalling department, relay complex junctions, provide adequate marshalling yards and rebuild big city stations further to enhance the operations of the LNWR which became, in the words of Sir Frederick Harrison, General Manager from 1893: '... the biggest undertaking in this country - if not the whole world. Indeed it is commonly believed to be the biggest joint-stock corporation in the world'.

However, Moon was not entirely consistent in his apportioning of money for some critical engineering features, particularly if he could not see a return on, or cost saving due to, the investment. The story of the brakes is a typical example, plus of course his insistence on locomotives having no more that six wheels. So long as train speeds were kept low braking was not such a crucial feature and so long as train weights were light 2-4-0s and 0-6-0s were man enough for the job, he reckoned. Thus problems were to ensue for Webb whilst he was around and stuck to these rigid requirements.

It is interesting to look at the values of maximum axle loading over the years from 1891 to 1903. The significant feature of these years was the absence of Sir Richard Moon from the scene, and the replacement of this cost-conscious Chairman by a more flexible hierarchy. In 1891 the highest axle loading was the 15 tons to be found on the 2-2-2-2 compound 'Greater Britain' class. In 1892 the three-cylinder compound 0-8-0 produced a

14 ton 8 cwt value, but then this load was the highest of the four coupled axles. Track limits were still restricting the maximum value, the accepted norm being 15 tons. However, by 1897 the new four-cylinder compound 4-4-0 produced a maximum of 18 tons and the four-cylinder compound 0-8-0 of 1901 that of 17 tons 4 cwt, so at least the adhesive weights were on the increase to cope with the higher train weights.

As regards the maximum axle loadings of other locomotives during Webb's time up to 1891, these ranged from the 11 tons 4 cwt of the 'Special DX' 0-6-0 to the 15 tons of the 'Watford Tank' 0-6-2T. The need to keep within the limits imposed by the Civil Engineering Department was the main reason for Webb locomotives being small in size, which kept their first cost down to an acceptable level. The Civil Engineering limits were caused by the Moon edict of minimising cost - lightweight track, which was cheaper, imposed a limit on axle loading calling for small engines, particularly if they were mostly limited to a maximum of six wheels. This philosophy was so ingrained in Frank Webb's locomotives over so many years, it is easy to understand how he persisted in his development of designs which were largely derived one from another. The commonality of parts thus engendered, although aiding cost minimisation, effectively held back the introduction of progressively heavier engines until a point was reached when it may have needed a new CME to achieve this. But Webb was, by that time, so set in his ways and so autocratic that no one could summon up the courage to question his rationale. Had Moon, in his days as Chairman, recognised the need for relaxing his rigid insistence on keeping costs down, matters might have moved forward and we could have seen 4-4-0s and 4-6-0s of both simple and compound types earlier. Whilst on the axle loading trends, little account seems to have been made of hammer blow additions to the static loads. Bearing in mind that the vast number of locomotives turned out by Crewe were two-cylinder simples, which tend to have high hammer blow loads due to the balance weights, one wonders how this affected the track condition adversely. Three- and four-cylinder designs were, by their layout, less likely to result in high hammer blow loadings, the latter, in ideal conditions, producing nil.

The fact remains, however, that within the constraints imposed upon him, Frank Webb did extraordinarily well to keep the LNWR locomotive stock at a pitch where it could cope with the demands placed upon it. After all, he was a first-class engineer and organizer, well capable of delivering the goods on time and at an acceptable cost. His handling of the Crewe works expansion and subsequent production capabilities played an important part in that and enabled the railway to rise to its reputation as 'The Premier Line'.

Sir Richard Moon and his wife, sons and daughters on a visit to Chester Place, *c.*1870s. Frank Webb standing second from right.   *Author's Collection*

Appendix Three

Frank Webb's Patents

Frank was a prolific producer of patents and barely a year went by between 1864 and 1902 without one, or more, patents being filed. The vast majority were connected with railway developments but a batch between 1867 and 1870, when he was at the Bolton Iron & Steel Works, involved iron and steel production. Of his total career between 1864 and 1902 only 5 years had no patent applications - 1866, 72, 80, 83 and 87.

His inventive genius places him as one of the leading, if not *the* leading, railway pioneer of his day. Many of his inventions were before their time and, as such, died before the full advantage could be taken of them. The double chimney was a case in point. It did have two blast-pipes but the draughting layout was different to that eventually adopted in BR days for some existing and new designs.

Concerning patents covering locomotive design, perhaps the most significant was the radial axle-box (British Patent No. 5052; 24th October, 1882). This was devised initially for the leading wheels of his 2-4-0s and gave a lateral movement of $1\frac{1}{4}$ inches either side of the centre-line. This was most successful, so much so that it was adopted for LNWR carriage stock as well. Also other railways adopted it on their locomotives, starting with the L&YR under Aspinall.

Despite his reputation for being egotistical about his work, with many of the patents another person was involved in the application, particularly for those allied to signalling developments. His colleague for these applications was A.M. Thompson (*see Chapter Four*).

One of the most significant patent applications was British Patent No. 167 of 12th January, 1877, which was for a system for automatically applying the brakes should a train pass a signal at danger or caution. This system also had additional features whereby an audible warning was given to the driver. This clearly was a very early form of Automatic Train Control (ATC), but was not adopted, or even tried. Why is not known, but one possibility is that the cost allied with the then current restricted speeds might well have blocked any investment being made available for its inception. After all at this time Moon was still controlling the purse-strings.

For this and many other inventions which were patented, with such a prolific mind and new ideas and designs always flowing, Frank could not have had the time to pursue many schemes any further. As regards ATC, it was to remain for Churchward on the GWR to bring in the first successful system some 30 years later.

Appendix Four

Locomotives Built under Webb

Type		Commonly known as	Years built	Number	Note
0-4-0T		2 ft 6 in. shunter	1880	10	
0-4-0ST		4 ft shunter	1872-92	20	a
0-4-2T		Dock Tank	1896-1902	20	
0-4-2CT		Crane Tank	1894	5	
2-2-2		Problem	1876-99	60	b
2-2-2-0	3cc	Experiment	1882-84	30	
2-2-2-0	3cc	Dreadnought	1884-86	40	
2-2-2-0	3cc	Teutonic	1889-90	10	
2-2-2-2	3cc	Greater Britain	1891-94	10	
2-2-2-2	3cc	John Hick	1894-98	10	
2-2-2-2T	3cc		1885	1	
4-2-2-0T	3cc		1884	1	c
2-2-2-2T	3cc		1887	1	
2-2-4-0T	3cc		1887	1	
2-4-0		Samson	1873-79	40	a
2-4-0		Newton	1872-73	20	a
2-4-0		Precursor	1874-79	40	
2-4-0		Precedent	1874-82	70	
2-4-0		Improved Precedent	1887-1901	158	
2-4-0		Whitworth	1889-96	90	d
2-4-0T			1876-80	50	
2-4-2T		4 ft 6 in.	1879-98	220	e
2-4-2T		5 ft 6 in.	1890-1897	160	f
4-4-0	4cc	Jubilee	1897-1900	40	
4-4-0	4cc	Alfred the Great	1901-1903	40	
0-6-0		DX	1872-73	86	a, h
0-6-0		Special DX	1881-98	500	g
0-6-0		17 in. Coal Engine	1873-1892	500	
0-6-0		Cauliflower	1880-1902	310	
0-6-0T		Special Tank	1871-80	240	a
0-6-2T		Coal Tank	1881-96	300	
0-6-2T		Watford Tank	1898-1902	80	
4-6-0	4cc	Bill Bailey	1903-05	30	
0-8-0			1892	1	i
0-8-0	3cc	A	1893-1900	110	
0-8-0	4cc	B	1901-05	170	

Notes

a To a Ramsbottom design.
b Rebuilds of original Ramsbottom designs. (The 'Problems' actually underwent two rebuilds of the whole class in the years specified above.)
c Converted from 'Metropolitan' tank No. 2063.
d Rebuilt from 'Samson' class.
e Forty of these were rebuilt from 2-4-0Ts.

f Forty of these were rebuilt from 'Precursors'
g Rebuilds of existing 'DX'.
h Built under Webb for L&YR.
i 2-cylinder simple later converted to 3-cylinder compound.

3cc 3-cylinder compound.
4cc 4-cylinder compound.

Appendix Five

Preserved Webb Locomotives

Type	No.	Name	Built	Date	Location
0-6-2T	1054		Crewe	1888	Keighley & Worth Valley Railway
2-4-0	790	*Hardwicke*	Crewe	1892	National Railway Museum

These two are the only survivors of a large fleet of Webb-designed locomotives and represent those prolific classes which undertook so much of the routine tasks on the LNWR.

During the Race to Aberdeen this engine made a record run with the 8. p. m. ex Euston, covering the distance between Crewe and Carlisle at an average speed of 67.2 miles per hour, 22nd August, 1895.

'Precedent' class No. 790 *Hardwicke*, which is now to be found preserved at the NRM. During the Race to Aberdeen this engine made a record run with the 8 pm ex-Euston, covering the distance between Crewe and Carlisle at an average speed of 67.2 miles per hour on 22nd August, 1895. *Author's Collection*

Bibliography

An Illustrated History of L&NWR Engines by E. Talbot, Ian Allan.

British Locomotives of the 20th Century by O.S. Nock, Patrick Stephens Ltd.

British Locomotive Practice & Performance by Charles Rous-Marten (extracts edited by Charles Fryer), Patrick Stephens Ltd.

Crewe Locomotive Works and its men by Brian Reed, David & Charles.

Experiments with Steam by Charles Fryer, Patrick Stephens Ltd.

'Francis William Webb, Chief Mechanical Engineer, London and North Western Railway 1871-1903; a survey of material for a study of his life and work'. Unpublished thesis by John E. Spink, October 1965.

'Handing on the Baton' by M. Rutherford, *Back Track*, Nov. 2002-Jan. 2003.

Illustrated Interviews, No. 31 - Mr Francis William Webb, *The Railway Magazine,* February 1900.

LMS 150 by Patrick Whitehouse and David St John Thomas, David & Charles.

L&NWR Locomotives - Part 2, by S. Cotterell & G.H. Wilkinson, RCTS.

Master Builders of Steam by H.A.V. Bulleid, Ian Allan.

Sir Nigel Gresley - The Engineer and his Family by Geoffrey Hughes, The Oakwood Press.

North Western - A Saga of the Premier Line of Great Britain: 1846-1922 by O.S. Nock, Ian Allan.

'Some Links in the Evolution of the Locomotive', extracts from the diaries of David Joy, *The Railway Magazine,* October 1908.

The Aspinall Era by H.A.V. Bulleid, Ian Allan.

The Compound Locomotive by J.T. van Riemsdijk, Atlantic Transport Publishers.

The Oxford Companion to British Railway History by Jack Simmons and Gordon Biddle (eds), Oxford University Press.

The Social and Economic Development of Crewe, 1870-1923 by Dr W.H. Chaloner, Manchester University Press, 1950.

The South Western Railway by C. Hamilton Ellis, George Allen & Unwin Ltd.

Trent Valley Magazine, May 1883.

Twenty Locomotive Men by C. Hamilton Ellis, Ian Allan.

Index

Numbers in **bold** type refer to illustrations.